STILL STEAMING

A Guide to Britain's Standard Gauge Steam Railways 2010-2011

EDITOR
John Robinson

Fourteenth Edition

RAILWAY LOCATOR MAP

The numbers shown on this map relate to the page numbers for each railway.
Pages 5-6 contain an alphabetical listing of the railways featured in this guide.
Please note that the markers on this map show the approximate location only.

ACKNOWLEDGEMENTS

We were greatly impressed by the friendly and cooperative manner of the staff and helpers of the railways which we selected to appear in this book, and wish to thank them all for the help they have given. In addition we wish to thank Bob Budd (cover design) and Michael Robinson (page layouts) for their help and also David Staines who has provided us with excellent photographs for several railways.

Although we believe that the information contained in this guide is accurate at the time of going to press, we, and the Railways and Museums itemised, are unable to accept liability for any loss, damage, distress or injury suffered as a result of any inaccuracies. Furthermore, we and the Railways are unable to guarantee operating and opening times which may always be subject to cancellation without notice.

If you feel we should include other locations or information in future editions, please let us know so that we may give them consideration. We would like to thank you for buying this guide and wish you 'Happy Steaming'!

John Robinson

John Robinson

EDITOR

Note: Further copies of our railway guides Still Steaming, Little Puffers and Tiny Trains plus our four new regional 'Full Steam Ahead' guides may be obtained, post free, from our address below or ordered on-line via our web site – www.stillsteaming.com

British Library Cataloguing in Publication Data
A catalogue record for this book is available from the British Library

ISBN-13: 978-1-86223-190-0

Copyright © 2010, MARKSMAN PUBLICATIONS. (01472 696226)
72 St. Peter's Avenue, Cleethorpes, N.E. Lincolnshire, DN35 8HU, England

Manufactured in the UK by The Cromwell Press Group

FOREWORD

Regular readers will notice that we have again expanded the number of railways featured in this guide with six new locations which were not included in our last edition. We are aware of the fact that several railways, notably, the Epping Ongar Railway and the Southall Railway Centre no longer appear in the guide but, as they are currently inoperative, we preferred to exclude them this time. The cover picture was kindly supplied by the Yeovil Railway Centre and features one of their Santa Special Guard Van trips.

CONTENTS

ALDERNEY RAILWAY

Address: P.O. Box 75, Alderney, Channel Islands GY9 3DA	**Nº of Steam Locos**: None at present
Telephone Nº: None	**Nº of Other Locos**: 2
Year Formed: 1978	**Nº of Members**: 50
Location of Line: Braye Harbour to Mannez Quarry, Alderney	**Annual Membership Fee**: £15.00
	Approx Nº of Visitors P.A.: 2,000+
Length of Line: 2 miles	**Gauge**: Standard
	Web site: www.alderneyrailway.com

Photo courtesy of David Staines

GENERAL INFORMATION

Nearest Mainline Station: Not applicable
Nearest Bus Station: Not applicable
Car Parking: Available on site
Coach Parking: Available on site
Souvenir Shop(s): Yes
Food & Drinks: None at the Railway itself but available nearby

SPECIAL INFORMATION

The original line was built during the 1840s to assist in the construction of the large breakwater in Braye Harbour and fortifications on the island.
The line itself opened in 1847 and was the first nationalised railway run by the Admiralty.

OPERATING INFORMATION

Opening Times: Weekends and Bank Holidays from Easter until the September with a Santa Special also running in December. Trains usually run at 2.30pm and 3.30pm but also at 4.00pm during July and August.
Steam Working: None at present
Prices: Adult Return £4.50
           Child Return   £3.00

Detailed Directions:
The Railway is situated adjacent to Braye Harbour.

Appleby Frodingham R.P.S.

Address: Appleby Frodingham Railway Preservation Society, P.O. Box 44, Brigg, North Lincolnshire   DN20 8XG
Telephone Nº: (01652) 656661
Year Formed: 1990
Location of Line: Corus Steelworks, Scunthorpe

Length of Line: 15 miles used on tours from almost 100 miles of track
Nº of Steam Locos: 2
Nº of Other Locos: 3
Nº of Members: 60
Gauge: Standard
Web site: www.afrps.co.uk

GENERAL INFORMATION

Nearest Mainline Station: Scunthorpe (1 mile)
Nearest Bus Station: Scunthorpe (½ mile)
Car Parking: Large free car park at the site
Coach Parking: At the site
Souvenir Shop(s): Yes – at the Loco Shed
Food & Drinks: Drinks/snacks served on train trips

SPECIAL INFORMATION

The Society operates 8 and 15 mile Rail and Brake Van tours of the Corus steelworks site (which covers almost 12 square miles) using its extensive internal railway system.

OPERATING INFORMATION

Opening Times: Selected weekends throughout the year which <u>must</u> be pre-booked via (01652) 657053 or e-mail – bookings@afrps.co.uk
Private Hire of a train is now available for parties and anniversaries with use of the Lounge coach.
Steam Working: Most active days. Ask for further details when booking.
Prices: Free – but the society relies on donations which are collected at the end of each tour.
Please note that children cannot be carried on Brake van tours due to the open verandahs.

Detailed Directions by Car:
Exit the M180 at Junction 4 and take the A18 into Scunthorpe. Turn right at the roundabout by Morrisons supermarket and follow the road along for approximately ½ mile. Turn right into Entrance E. Car parking is available on the left and the path to the station is on the right.

AVON VALLEY RAILWAY

Address: Bitton Station, Bath Road, Bitton, Bristol BS30 6HD **Telephone Nº:** (0117) 932-5538 **Year Formed:** 1973 **Location of Line:** Midway between Bristol and Bath on A431 **Length of Line:** 3 miles	**Nº of Steam Locos:** 6 **Nº of Other Locos:** 5 **Nº of Members:** Approximately 700 **Annual Membership Fee:** £15.00 **Approx Nº of Visitors P.A.:** 80,000 **Gauge:** Standard **Web site:** www.avonvalleyrailway.org

GENERAL INFO

Nearest Mainline Station: Keynsham (1½ miles)
Nearest Bus Station: Bristol or Bath (7 miles)
Car Parking: Available at Bitton Station
Coach Parking: Available at Bitton Station
Souvenir Shop(s): Yes
Food & Drinks: Yes

SPECIAL INFO

The line has been extended through the scenic Avon Valley towards Bath and a new platform is now open linking with boat trips along the River Avon.

OPERATING INFO

Opening Times: Every Sunday and some Saturdays from Easter to October and on weekends during December. Also Bank Holiday Mondays, Wednesdays in June and July and Tuesdays to Thursdays during School Holidays. Also open for Santa Specials over Christmas. Open 10.30am to 5.00pm.
Steam Working: 11.00am to 4.00pm
Prices: Adult £6.00
Child £4.50
Family Tickets £16.50
Senior Citizens £5.00

Detailed Directions by Car:
From All Parts: Exit the M4 at Junction 18. Follow the A46 towards Bath and at the junction with the A420 turn right towards Bristol. At Bridge Yate turn left onto the A4175 and continue until you reach the A431. Turn right and Bitton Station is 100 yards on the right.

BARROW HILL ROUNDHOUSE RAILWAY CENTRE

Address: Barrow Hill Roundhouse, Campbell Drive, Barrow Hill, Staveley, Chesterfield   S43 2PR
Telephone Nº: (01246) 472450
Year Formed: 1998
Location: Staveley, near Chesterfield
Length of Line: ¾ mile

Nº of Steam Locos: 9
Nº of Other Locos: Over 40
Nº of Members: Approximately 400
Annual Membership Fee: £16.00 (Adult)
Approx Nº of Visitors P.A.: 30,000
Gauge: Standard
Web site: www.barrowhill.org

GENERAL INFORMATION

Nearest Mainline Station:
Chesterfield (3½ miles)
Nearest Bus Station:
Chesterfield (3 miles)
Car Parking: Space available for 300 cars
Coach Parking: Available
Souvenir Shop(s): Yes
Food & Drinks: Yes – buffet

SPECIAL INFORMATION

Britain's last remaining operational railway roundhouse provides storage and repair facilities for standard gauge steam, diesel and electric locomotives.

OPERATING INFORMATION

Opening Times: Open at weekends throughout the year from 10.00am to 4.00pm.
Steam Working: Special open days only. 2010 dates – Rail Ale Festival on 21st & 22nd May; Santa Steam Trains on 12th and 19th December.
Please phone for further details or check the railway's web site.
Prices: Please phone for prices.

Detailed Directions by Car:
Exit the M1 at Junction 30 and take the A619 to Staveley (about 3½ miles). Pass through Staveley, turn right at Troughbrook onto 'Works Road'. Continue along for ¾ mile, pass under the railway bridge and take the turn immediately on the right. Turn left onto Campbell Drive and the Roundhouse is on the left. The railway is signposted with Brown Tourist signs.

THE BATTLEFIELD LINE

Address: The Battlefield Line,
Shackerstone Station, Shackerstone,
Warwickshire   CV13 6NW
Telephone Nº: (01827) 880754
Year Formed: 1968
Location of Line: North West of Market
Bosworth
Length of Line: 5 miles

Nº of Steam Locos: 5
Nº of Other Locos: 23
Nº of Members: 500 approximately
Annual Membership Fee: £15.00 Adult;
£25.00 Family
Approx Nº of Visitors P.A.: 50,000
Gauge: Standard
Web site: www.battlefield-line-railway.co.uk

GENERAL INFORMATION

Nearest Mainline Station: Nuneaton (9 miles)
Nearest Bus Station: Nuneaton & Hinckley (9 miles)
Car Parking: Ample free parking available
Coach Parking: Can cater for coach parties
Souvenir Shop(s): Yes
Food & Drinks: Yes – Station Buffet

SPECIAL INFORMATION

Travel from the Grade II listed Shackerstone Station
through the beautiful Leicestershire countryside
with views of the adjoining Ashby Canal. Arrive at
the award-winning Shenton Station and explore
Bosworth Battlefield (1485) before making the
return journey.

OPERATING INFORMATION

Operating Info: 2010 dates: Weekends and Bank
Holidays from 20th March to 31st October and
Santa Specials on weekends from 4th December to
Christmas Eve. Also open on Wednesday afternoons
in July and August. Please check the web site for
further details.
Opening Times: 10.55am to 5.10pm
Steam Working: From 11.30am to 4.00pm during
high season and Sundays.
Prices: Adult Return £8.00
Child Return £5.00 (ages 5-15 years)
O.A.P. Return £6.50
Family Ticket £24.00
(2 adults and 2 children)

Detailed Directions by Car:
Follow the brown tourist signs from the A444 or A447 heading towards the market town of Market Bosworth.
Continue towards the villages of Congerstone & Shackerstone and finally to Shackerstone Station. Access is only
available via the Old Trackbed.

BEAMISH –
THE LIVING MUSEUM OF THE NORTH

Address: Beamish – The Living Museum of the North, Co. Durham   DH9 0RG
Telephone N°: (0191) 370-4000
Year Formed: 1970
Length of Line: ½ mile

N° of Steam Locos: 8
N° of Other Locos: 2
N.B.: Not all Locos are on display
Approx N° of Visitors P.A.: 320,000
Web site: www.beamish.org.uk

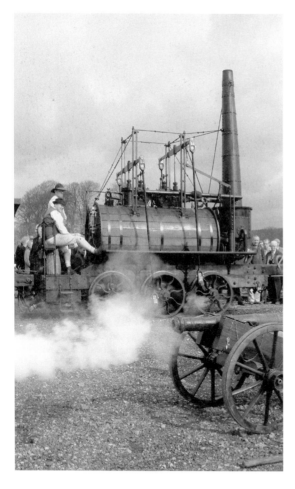

GENERAL INFORMATION

Nearest Mainline Station: Newcastle Central (8 miles); Durham City (12 miles)
Nearest Bus Station: Durham (12 miles), Newcastle (8 miles)
Car Parking: Free parking for 2,000 cars
Coach Parking: Free parking for 40 coaches
Souvenir Shop(s): Yes
Food & Drinks: Yes – self service tea room, licensed period Public House and a Coffee shop.

SPECIAL INFORMATION

A replica of William Hedley's famous 1813 locomotive "Puffing Billy" steams on the Pockerley Waggonway at Beamish alongside replicas of Locomotion and the Steam Elephant.

OPERATING INFORMATION

Opening Times: Open all year round: from 10.00am to 4.00pm in the Winter (November to March). Closed on Mondays and Fridays in the Winter. Open from 10.00am to 5.00pm during the Summer (April to October). Check for Christmas opening times.
N.B. Winter visits are centred on the Town and Tramway only. Other areas are closed and admission prices are reduced.
Allow 4-5 hours for a Summer visit and two hours in the Winter.
Steam Working: Daily during the Summer
Prices:
Adult £16.00 in Summer; £7.50 in Winter
Child £10.00 in Summer; £6.00 in Winter
O.A.P. £13.00 in Summer; £7.50 in Winter
Children under 5 are admitted free.
Special Family Tickets are available.
Prices are higher than Winter at Christmas.

Detailed Directions by Car:
From North & South: Follow the A1(M) to Junction 63 (Chester-le-street) and then take A693 for 4 miles towards Stanley; From North-West: Take the A68 south to Castleside near Consett and follow the signs on the A692 and A693 via Stanley.

THE BLUEBELL RAILWAY

Address: The Bluebell Railway, Sheffield Park Station, Nr. Uckfield, East Sussex, TN22 3QL
Telephone No: (01825) 720800
Information Line: (01825) 720825
Year Formed: 1959
Location of Line: Nr. Uckfield, E. Sussex
Length of Line: 9 miles

No of Steam Locos: Over 30 with up to 3 in operation on any given day
No of Other Locos: –
No of Members: 10,000
Annual Membership Fee: £20.00 Adult
Approx No of Visitors P.A.: 175,000
Gauge: Standard
Web site: www.bluebell-railway.co.uk

Photo courtesy of David Staines

GENERAL INFORMATION

Nearest Mainline Station: East Grinstead (2 miles) with a bus connection
Nearest Bus Station: East Grinstead
Car Parking: Parking at Sheffield Park and Horsted Keynes Stations.
Coach Parking: Sheffield Park is best
Souvenir Shop(s): Yes
Food & Drinks: Yes – buffets and licensed bars & restaurant

SPECIAL INFORMATION

The Railway runs 'Golden Arrow' dining trains on Saturday evenings and Sunday lunchtimes. There is also a museum and model railway at Sheffield Park Station.

OPERATING INFORMATION

Opening Times: 2010 dates: Open every weekend throughout the year and also daily from 2nd April to 7th November inclusive. Also open during School holidays and for Santa Specials during December. Open from approximately 10.30am to 5.30pm
Steam Working: As above
Prices: Adult Return £12.00
  Child Return £6.00
  Family Return £33.00 (2 adult + 3 child)

Detailed Directions by Car:
Sheffield Park Station is situated on the A275 Wych Cross to Lewes road. Horsted Keynes Station is signposted from the B2028 Lingfield to Haywards Heath road.

BODMIN & WENFORD RAILWAY

Address: Bodmin General Station, Losthwithiel Road, Bodmin, Cornwall PL31 1AQ
Telephone Nº: (0845) 1259678
Year Formed: 1984
Location of Line: Bodmin Parkway Station to Bodmin General & Boscarne Junction.
Length of Line: 6½ miles

Nº of Steam Locos: 11
Nº of Other Locos: 9
Nº of Members: 1,200
Annual Membership Fee: £14.00
Approx Nº of Visitors P.A.: 53,000
Gauge: Standard
Web: www.bodminandwenfordrailway.co.uk

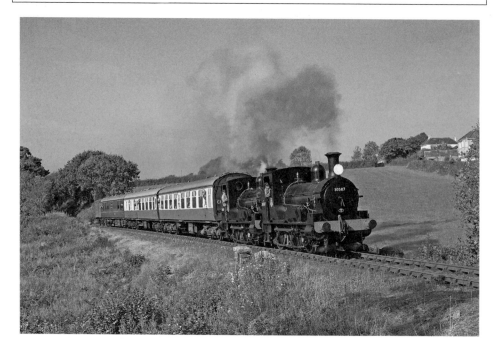

GENERAL INFORMATION

Nearest Mainline Station: Bodmin Parkway (cross platform interchange with the Bodmin & Wenford Railway)
Car Parking: Free parking at Bodmin General
Coach Parking: Free parking at Bodmin General
Souvenir Shop(s): Yes
Food & Drinks: Yes

SPECIAL INFORMATION

The Railway has steep gradients and there are two different branches to choose from Bodmin General. Through tickets to "Bodmin & Wenford Railway" are available from all Mainline stations.

OPERATING INFORMATION

Opening Times: 2010 dates: Daily from 29th May to 3rd October. Also daily during Easter week. Open other selected dates from February to May + October and Santa Specials on 4th, 5th, 11th, 12th, 18th, 19th, 24th, 26th, 27th, 28th & 31st December. Open 10.00am – 5.00pm on most days.
Steam Working: Most trains are steam-hauled except for most Saturdays when Diesels are used. Daily steam throughout August.
Prices: Adult All Day Rover £11.50
Child All Day Rover £6.00 (Under-3s free)
Family Day Rover £30.00
(2 adult + 2 child or 1 adult + 4 child)

Detailed Directions by Car:
From the A30/A38/A389 follow the signs to Bodmin Town Centre then follow the brown tourist signs to the Steam Railway on the B3268 Losthwithiel Road.

BO'NESS & KINNEIL RAILWAY

Address: Bo'ness Station, Union Street, Bo'ness, West Lothian EH51 9AQ	**Nº of Steam Locos**: 26
Telephone Nº: (01506) 822298	**Nº of Other Locos**: 25
Year Opened: 1981	**Nº of Members**: 1,300
Location of Line: Bo'ness to Manuel	**Annual Membership Fee**: £17.00
Length of Line: 5 miles	**Approx Nº of Visitors P.A.**: 70,000
	Gauge: Standard
	Web site: www.srps.org.uk

GENERAL INFORMATION

Nearest Mainline Station: Linlithgow (3 miles)
Nearest Bus Station: Bo'ness (¼ mile)
Car Parking: Free parking at Bo'ness and Birkhill Stations
Coach Parking: Free parking at Bo'ness Station
Souvenir Shop(s): Yes
Food & Drinks: Yes

SPECIAL INFORMATION

The Railway (which is operated by volunteers from the Scottish Railway Preservation Society) runs from Bo'ness to Birkhill where guided tours of the Birkhill Fireclay Mine are available and the new extension to Manuel crosses the impressive Avon Viaduct.

OPERATING INFORMATION

Opening Times: 2010 dates: Open on weekends from 27th March to 31st October. Also open daily from 6th July to 29th August.
Steam Working: The first train leaves at 10.45am and is steam-hauled as are all trains until the 3.30pm service. The last train leaves at 4.45pm and is diesel-hauled.
Prices: Adult Return £8.00   Child Return £4.00 Family Return £20.00   Concession Return £7.00
N.B. Group discounts are also available – please phone for further details. Also, special fares and timetables apply for special events.

Detailed Directions by Car:
From Edinburgh: Take the M9 and exit at Junction 3. Then take the A904 to Bo'ness; From Glasgow: Take the M80 to M876 and then M9 (South). Exit at Junction 5 and take A904 to Bo'ness; From the North: Take M9 (South), exit at Junction 5, then take A904 to Bo'ness; From Fife: Leave the A90 after the Forth Bridge, then take A904 to Bo'ness.

BOWES RAILWAY

Address: Bowes Railway, Springwell Village, Gateshead, Tyne & Wear NE9 7QJ **Telephone Nº**: (0191) 416-1847 **Year Formed**: 1976 **Location of Line**: Springwell Village **Length of Line**: 1¼ miles	**Nº of Steam Locos**: 2 **Nº of Other Locos**: 4 **Nº of Members**: Approximately 70 **Annual Membership Fee**: £15.00 **Approx Nº of Visitors P.A.**: 5,000 **Gauge**: Standard **Web site**: www.bowesrailway.co.uk

GENERAL INFORMATION

Nearest Mainline Station: Newcastle Central (3 miles)
Nearest Bus Station: Gateshead Interchange (2 miles)
Car Parking: Free parking at site
Coach Parking: Free parking at site
Souvenir Shop(s): Yes
Food & Drinks: Yes

SPECIAL INFORMATION

Designed by George Stephenson and opened in 1826, the Railway is a scheduled Ancient Monument which operates unique preserved standard gauge rope-hauled inclines and steam hauled passenger trains.

OPERATING INFORMATION

Opening Times: The Springwell site is open for static viewing (no charges) on weekdays and some Saturdays throughout the year – 10.00am to 3.00pm.
Steam Working: As the 2010/2011 timetable had not been agreed when this book went to press, we suggest that readers check the railway's web site or contact the railway directly for further information.
Prices: No charges for visting but admission fees are charged for special events. Please contact the railway or check the web site for further details.

Detailed Directions by Car:
From A1 (Northbound): Follow the A194(M) to the Tyne Tunnel and turn left at the sign for Springwell.
From A1 (Southbound): Take the turn off left for the B1288 to Springwell and Wrekenton.

BRESSINGHAM STEAM EXPERIENCE

Address: Bressingham Steam Museum, Bressingham, Diss, Norfolk IP22 2AB
Telephone Nº: (01379) 686900
Year Formed: Mid 1950's
Location of Line: Bressingham, Near Diss
Length of Line: 5 miles in total (3 lines)

Nº of Steam Locos: Many Steam locos
Nº of Members: 70 volunteers
Annual Membership Fee: –
Approx Nº of Visitors P.A.: 80,000+
Gauge: Standard, 2 foot, 10¼ inches and 15 inches
Web site: www.bressingham.co.uk

GENERAL INFORMATION

Nearest Mainline Station: Diss (2½ miles)
Nearest Bus Station: Bressingham (1¼ miles)
Car Parking: Free parking for 400 cars available
Coach Parking: Free parking for 30 coaches
Souvenir Shop(s): Yes
Food & Drinks: Yes

SPECIAL INFORMATION

In addition to Steam locomotives, Bressingham has a large selection of steam traction engines, fixed steam engines and also the National Dad's Army Museum, two extensive gardens and a water garden centre.

OPERATING INFORMATION

Opening Times: 2010 dates: Daily from 27th March to 31st October. Open from 10.30am to 5.00pm and until 5.30pm in June, July and August.
Steam Working: Almost every operating day except for most Mondays and Tuesdays in March, April, May, June, July, September and October. Please phone the Museum for further details.
Prices: Adult £9.50 (non-Steam) £12.00 (Steam)
Child £6.50 (non-Steam) £8.00 (Steam)
Family £27 (non-Steam) £35.00 (Steam)
Seniors £9.00 (non-Steam) £10.50 (Steam)

Detailed Directions by Car:
From All Parts: Take the A11 to Thetford and then follow the A1066 towards Diss for Bressingham. The Museum is signposted by the brown tourist signs.

BRISTOL HARBOUR RAILWAY

Address: Princes Wharf, City Docks, Bristol BS1 4RN	**N° of Steam Locos:** 2
Telephone N°: (0117) 903-1570	**N° of Other Locos:** 1
Year Formed: 1978	**N° of Members:** –
Location of Line: South side of the Floating Harbour	**Annual Membership Fee:** –
	Approx N° of Visitors P.A.: –
	Gauge: Standard
Length of Line: 1½ miles	**Web site:** None

GENERAL INFORMATION

Nearest Mainline Station: Bristol Temple Meads (1 mile)
Nearest Bus Station: City Centre (½ mile)
Car Parking: None at present
Coach Parking: None at present
Souvenir Shop(s): None at present
Food & Drinks: Cafes available near the Railway

SPECIAL INFORMATION

Although the Bristol Industrial Museum is currently closed, the railway continues to operate on a limited basis between S.S. Great Britain and Cumberland Basin during 2010. Platforms are located at the Create Centre and the SS Great Britain.

OPERATING INFORMATION

Opening Times: 2010 dates: 20th & 21st March; 3rd, 4th, 5th, 17th & 18th April; 1st, 2nd, 3rd, 29th, 30th & 21st May; 19th & 20th June; 10th, 11th & 31st July; 1st, 28th, 29th & 30th August; 11th & 12th September; 2nd, 3rd, 23rd, 24th, 30th & 31st October. Trains run from 11.00am to 5.00pm.
Steam Working: Please contact the railway for further details.
Prices: Return £3.00
　　　　　 Single £2.00
Note: Children under the age of 6 travel for free.

Detailed Directions by Car:
From All Parts: Follow signs to Bristol City Centre and then the Brown Tourist signs for the Museum. A good landmark to look out for are the 4 huge quayside cranes.

BUCKINGHAMSHIRE RAILWAY CENTRE

Address: Quainton Road Station, Quainton, Aylesbury, Bucks. HP22 4BY	**N° of Steam Locos**: 30
Telephone N°: (01296) 655720	**N° of Other Locos**: 6
Year Formed: 1969	**N° of Members**: 1,000
Location of Line: At Quainton on the old Metropolitan/Great Central Line	**Annual Membership Fee**: £20.00
	Approx N° of Visitors P.A.: 40,000
	Gauge: Standard (also a Miniature line)
Length of Line: 2 × ½ mile demo tracks	**Recorded Info. Line**: (01296) 655450

GENERAL INFORMATION

Nearest Mainline Station: Aylesbury (6 miles)
Nearest Bus Station: Aylesbury
Car Parking: Free parking for 500 cars available
Coach Parking: Free parking for 10 coaches
Souvenir Shop(s): Yes
Food & Drinks: Yes

SPECIAL INFORMATION

In addition to a large collection of locomotives and carriages, the Centre has an extensive ½ mile outdoor miniature railway system operated by the Vale of Aylesbury Model Engineering Society.

Web site: www.bucksrailcentre.org

OPERATING INFORMATION

Opening Times: Daily for restricted viewing from Easter to October and for less restricted static viewing on Saturdays. Open 10.30am to 4.30pm.
Steam Working: Sundays and Bank Holidays from April to October and also on Wednesdays during the School holidays.
Prices: Adult £5.50, £8.00 and £9.00
Child £3.00, £5.00 and £6.00
(Under 5's travel free of charge)
Senior Citizen £5.00, £7.00 and £8.00
Family £14.00, £21.00 and £24.00
(2 adults + up to 4 children)
Note: Prices shown above are for static viewing, Steam Days and Special Event days respectively.

Detailed Directions by Car:
The Buckinghamshire Railway Centre is signposted off the A41 Aylesbury to Bicester Road at Waddesdon and off the A413 Buckingham to Aylesbury road at Whitchurch. Junctions 7, 8 and 9 of the M40 are all close by.

CALEDONIAN RAILWAY

Address: The Station, 2 Park Road, Brechin, Angus DD9 7AF
Telephone Nº: (01561) 377760
Year Formed: 1979
Location of Line: From Brechin to the Bridge of Dun
Length of Line: 4 miles

Nº of Steam Locos: 5
Nº of Other Locos: 10
Nº of Members: 250
Annual Membership Fee: Adult £12.00; Family £15.00; OAP/Junior £5.00
Approx Nº of Visitors P.A.: 12,000
Gauge: Standard
Web site: www.caledonianrailway.com

GENERAL INFORMATION

Nearest Mainline Station: Montrose (4½ miles)
Nearest Bus Station: Brechin (200 yards)
Car Parking: Ample free parking at both Stations
Coach Parking: Free parking at both Stations
Souvenir Shop(s): Yes
Food & Drinks: Light refreshments are available

SPECIAL INFORMATION

Brechin Station is the only original Terminus station in preservation.

OPERATING INFORMATION

Opening Times: 2010 dates: Easter specials on 3rd & 4th April; Christmas specials in December and every Sunday from 30th May to 5th September. Also some Saturdays in July and August and for other Special Events throughout the year. Please contact the Railway for further details. Trains usually run from 10.30am to 5.05pm.
Steam Working: Steam service on every Sunday.
Prices: Adult Return £5.00   Child Return £3.00
          Senior Citizen Return £4.00
          Family Return £16.00 (2 adult + 3 child)
Group discounts are available if booked in advance.

Detailed Directions by Car:
From South: For Brechin Station, leave the A90 at the Brechin turn-off and go straight through the Town Centre. Pass the Northern Hotel, take the 2nd exit at the mini-roundabout then it is 150 yards to Park Road/St. Ninian Square; From North: For Brechin Station, leave the A90 at the Brechin turn-off and go straight through Trinity Village. Turn left at the mini-roundabout, it is then 250 yards to Park Road/St. Ninian Square. Bridge of Dun is situated half way between Brechin and Montrose. (Follow tourist signs).

CAMBRIAN HERITAGE RAILWAYS

Address: Cambrian Railways Trust, Llynclys South Station, Llynclys, Oswestry, Shropshire SY10 8BX	**Nº of Steam Locos**: 2 (1 in operation)
	Nº of Other Locos: 2
	Nº of Members: 200+
Telephone Nº: (01691) 679007	**Annual Membership Fee**: £12.00
Year Formed: 1997	**Approx Nº of Visitors P.A.**: 2,500
Location of Line: Llynclys, Oswestry	**Gauge**: Standard
Length of Line: Approximately ¾ mile	**Web site**: www.cambrianrailways.com

GENERAL INFORMATION

Nearest Mainline Station: Gobowen (7 miles)
Nearest Bus Station: Oswestry (5 miles)
Car Parking: Limited parking available on site
Coach Parking: Limited park available on site
Souvenir Shop(s): Yes
Food & Drinks: Available

SPECIAL INFORMATION

In 2007, the Cambrian Railway Trust ran their first steam service. This was the first steam train on the line for more than 40 years! The Trust ultimately aims to extend the line to run a regular passenger service from Llynclys wharf to Pen-y-Garreg Lane.

OPERATING INFORMATION

Opening Times: 2010 dates: Open every Saturday, Sunday and Bank Holiday from Easter to the 26th September. Also open on Sundays in October and December. Trains run from 11.00am to 4.00pm.
Steam Working: Please contact the Railway for information.
Prices: Adults £4.50 (Steam) £2.50 (Diesel)
Concessions £2.50 (Steam) £1.00 (Diesel)
Family £12.00 (Steam) £6.00 (Diesel)
Note: All the above are "Full Day Rover" tickets.

Detailed Directions by Car:
The Railway is situated on the B4396 approximately 5 miles southwest of Oswestry, just off the A483 heading towards Welshpool. Turn left at Llyncly Crossroads towards Knockin. The entrance to the site is on the right after about 400 yards, immediately over the railway bridge.

CHASEWATER RAILWAY

Address: Chasewater Country Park, Pool Road, Near Brownhills, Staffs, WS8 7NL
Telephone Nº: (01543) 452623
Year Re-formed: 1985
Location of Line: Chasewater Country Park, Brownhills, near Walsall
Length of Line: 2 miles

Nº of Steam Locos: 10
Nº of Other Locos: 12
Nº of Members: 800
Annual Membership Fee: Adult £15.00; Family £20.00; Concessions £10.00
Approx Nº of Visitors P.A.: 46,000
Gauge: Standard
Web site: www.chaserail.com

GENERAL INFORMATION

Nearest Mainline Station: Walsall or Birmingham (both approximately 8 miles)
Nearest Bus Station: Walsall or Birmingham
Car Parking: Free parking in Chasewater Park
Coach Parking: Free parking in Chasewater Park
Souvenir Shop(s): Yes
Food & Drinks: Yes

SPECIAL INFORMATION

Chasewater Railway is based on the Cannock Chase & Wolverhampton Railway opened in 1856. The railway passed into the hands of the National Coal Board which then ceased using the line in 1965. Trains operate between Brownhills West and Chasetown.

OPERATING INFORMATION

Opening Times: 2010 dates: Sundays and Bank Holiday Mondays throughout the year plus most Saturdays from 22nd May to 11th September and Tuesdays and Thursdays from 27th July to 2nd September. Also Santa Specials in December. A regular service runs from 11.00am on operating days.

Steam Working: Please check the web site or phone for further details.

Prices: Adult Return £3.45
             Child Return £2.45
             Family Return £8.45

All tickets offer unlimited rides on the day of issue.

Detailed Directions by Car:
Chasewater Country Park is situated in Brownhills off the A5 southbound near the junction of the A5 with the A452 Chester Road. Follow the Brown tourist signs on the A5 for the Country Park.

CHATHAM HISTORIC DOCKYARD RAILWAY

Address: Dock Road, Chatham
Telephone N°: (01634) 823800
Year Formed: 2001
Location of Line: Chatham, Kent
Length of Line: ¾ mile

N° of Steam Locos: 5
N° of Other Locos: 3
N° of Members: –
Approx N° of Visitors P.A.: Not known
Gauge: Standard
Web site: www.thedockyardrailway.co.uk

GENERAL INFORMATION

Nearest Mainline Station: Chatham (1½ miles)
Nearest Bus Station: Gillingham (1½ miles)
Car Parking: Available on site
Coach Parking: Available
Souvenir Shop(s): Yes
Food & Drinks: Available

SPECIAL INFORMATION

The Dockyard Railway is operated by North Kent
Industrial Locomotive Society and runs
demonstrations of freight steaming at Chatham's
Historic Dockyard (www.chdt.org.uk).

OPERATING INFORMATION

Opening Times: Open one weekend per month.
Please telephone or check the web site for details of
special event dates.
Steam Working: Most operating days. Please note
that the Railway does not offer train rides, merely
demonstrations of engines in operation.
Prices: Adults £15.00
Children (Aged 5-15 years old) £10.50
Concessions £12.50
Family Tickets £42.50
Note: Prices shown are for admission to the
Dockyard and tickets are valid for 12 months.
However, entrance to some special events is an
additional charge.

Detailed Directions by Car:
From All Parts: Exit the M2 at Junction 3 and follow the A229 to Chatham. Follow the Brown tourist signs which
clearly mark the correct route to the Dockyard.

CHINNOR & PRINCES RISBOROUGH RAILWAY

Address: Station Road, Chinnor, Oxon, OX39 4ER
Telephone Nº: (01844) 353535 (timetable)
Year Formed: 1989
Location: The Icknield Line, Chinnor
Length of Line: 3½ miles
Gauge: Standard

Nº of Steam Locos: 1
Nº of Other Locos: 6
Nº of Members: 1,000
Annual Membership Fee: Adult £13.00; Family £20.00; Child £5.00; OAP £8.00
Approx Nº of Visitors P.A.: 15,000
Web Site: www.chinnorrailway.co.uk

Photo courtesy of Peter Harris

GENERAL INFORMATION

Nearest Mainline Station: Princes Risborough (4 miles)
Nearest Bus Station: High Wycombe (10 miles)
Car Parking: Free parking at site
Coach Parking: Prior arrangement preferred but not necessary
Souvenir Shop(s): Yes
Food & Drinks: Soft drinks and light snacks in Station Buffet. Buffet usually available on trains.

SPECIAL INFORMATION

The Chinnor & Princes Risborough Railway operates the remaining 3½ mile section of the former GWR Watlington Branch from Chinnor to Thame Junction.

OPERATING INFORMATION

Opening Times: 2010 dates: Sundays and Bank Holiday Mondays from 14th March to 31st October and also Santa Specials on weekends in December. Also open on selected Saturdays between April and August. Please check the railway's website for details.
Steam Working: Operates from 10.15am to 4.15pm on Sundays.
Prices: Adult Return £9.00
Child Return £4.50
Family Return £22.50 (2 adult + 2 child)
Senior Citizen Return £8.00

Detailed Directions by Car:
From All Parts: The railway at Chinnor is situated in Station Road just off the B4009. Junction 6 of the M40 is 4 miles away and Princes Risborough 4 miles further along the B4009. Once in Chinnor follow the brown Tourist signs to the railway.

CHOLSEY & WALLINGFORD RAILWAY

Address: Wallingford Station,
5 Hithercroft Road, Wallingford, Oxon,
OX10 9GQ
Telephone Nº: (01491) 835067 (24hr info)
Year Formed: 1981
Location of Line: Wallingford, Oxon.
Length of Line: 2½ miles

Nº of Steam Locos: Visiting locos only
Nº of Other Locos: 4
Nº of Members: 250
Annual Membership Fee: £12.50
Approx Nº of Visitors P.A.: 9,700
Gauge: Standard
Web: www.cholsey-wallingford-railway.com

GENERAL INFORMATION

Nearest Mainline Station: Joint station at Cholsey
Nearest Bus Station: Wallingford (¼ mile)
Car Parking: Off road parking available
Coach Parking: Off road parking available
Souvenir Shop(s): Yes
Food & Drinks: Yes

SPECIAL INFORMATION

The Wallingford branch (now known as "The Bunk Line") was originally intended as a through line to Princes Risborough, via Watlington, but became the first standard gauge branch of Brunel's broad-gauge London to Bristol line.

OPERATING INFORMATION

Opening Times: Selected weekends from Easter until Christmas with trains running from 11.00am to 4.30pm – please phone the railway or check the web site for further details.
Steam Working: The railway will have a visiting steam locomotive which will commence operation from June 2010. Please contact the railway for further information.
Prices: Adult Return £6.00
　　　　　 Child Return £3.00
　　　　　 Concessionary Return £5.00
　　　　　 Family Return £16.00 (2 adult + 2 child)
Prices: Prices may be subject to change for Engine visits and other special events.

Detailed Directions by Car:
From All Parts: Exit from the A34 at the Milton Interchange (between E. Ilsley and Abingdon). Follow signs to Didcot and Wallingford (A4130). Take Wallingford bypass, then turn left at the first roundabout (signposted Hithercroft Road). The Station is then ½ mile on the right.

CHURNET VALLEY RAILWAY

Address: The Railway Station, Cheddleton, Leek, Staffs. ST13 7EE **Telephone Nº:** (01538) 360522 **Year Formed:** 1978 **Location of Line:** Cheddleton to Froghall **Length of Line:** 5½ miles	**Nº of Steam Locos:** 2 **Nº of Other Locos:** 3 **Nº of Members:** – **Annual Membership Fee:** £14.00 **Approx Nº of Visitors P.A.:** 70,000 **Gauge:** Standard **Web site:** www.churnetvalleyrailway.co.uk

GENERAL INFORMATION

Nearest Mainline Station: Stoke-on-Trent (12 miles)
Nearest Bus Station: Leek (5 miles)
Car Parking: Parking available on site
Coach Parking: Restricted space – please book in advance
Souvenir Shop(s): Yes
Food & Drinks: Yes

SPECIAL INFORMATION

Cheddleton Station is a Grade II listed building, Consall is a sleepy halt with Victorian charm, whereas Kingsley & Froghall has been rebuilt in NSR style and includes disabled facilities and a tearoom.

OPERATING INFORMATION

Opening Times: 2010 dates: Weekends and Bank Holidays from 2nd April to 10th October. Also open on Wednesdays in July, August and December and on weekends in December. Trains run from 10.30am on most operating days or from 10.00am on Bank Holidays and Special Event days.
Steam Working: Sundays from March to October, Saturdays from May to September, Wednesdays in July and August and all Bank Holiday Mondays. Also various other special events throughout the year.
Prices: Please telephone (01538) 360522 for details or check the railway's web site.

Detailed Directions by Car:
From All Parts: Take the M6 to Stoke-on-Trent and follow trunk roads to Leek. Cheddleton Station is just off the A520 Leek to Stone road. Kingsley & Froghall Station is just off the A52 Ashbourne Road.

COLEFORD GWR MUSEUM

Address: The Old Railway Station, Railway Drive, Coleford GL16 8RH **Telephone Nº:** (01594) 833569 **Year Formed:** 1988 **Location of Line:** Coleford **Length of Line:** 100 yards	**Nº of Steam Locos:** 2 **Nº of Other Locos:** – **Nº of Members:** – **Approx Nº of Visitors P.A.:** Not known **Gauge:** 7¼ inches and Standard gauge **Web site:** www.colefordgwr.150m.com

GENERAL INFORMATION

Nearest Mainline Station: Lydney (7½ miles)
Nearest Bus Station: Gloucester (20 miles)
Car Parking: Available on site
Coach Parking: Available on site
Souvenir Shop(s): Yes
Food & Drinks: Tea and Coffee available only

SPECIAL INFORMATION

Based in the 1883 Goods Shed at Coleford, the Museum chronicles the history of railways in the Forest of Dean.

OPERATING INFORMATION

Opening Times: Friday and Saturday afternoons and Bank Holidays throughout the year. Open from 2.30pm to 5.00pm and at other times by prior arrangement.
Steam Working: Easter Monday and other Bank Holidays. Please contact the Museum for details.
Prices: Adults £3.00 (admission to the museum)
  Children £1.50 (admission to the museum)
  Miniature Railway Rides £1.50
  Peckett Footplate Visit £2.00 (if steaming)

Detailed Directions by Car:
From All Parts: From the M50 take the A40 at Ross-on-Wye to Monmouth then the A4136 towards Cinderford. Turn off the A4136 into Coleford and the Museum is located in the Town Centre.

COLNE VALLEY RAILWAY

Address: Castle Hedingham Station,
Yeldham Road, Castle Hedingham, Essex,
CO9 3DZ
Telephone Nº: (01787) 461174
Year Formed: 1974
Location of Line: On A1017, 7 miles
north-west of Braintree
Length of Line: Approximately 1 mile

Nº of Steam Locos: 4
Nº of Other Locos: 11
Nº of Members: 280
Annual Membership Fee: £11.00
Approx Nº of Visitors P.A.: 45,000
Gauge: Standard
Web Site: www.colnevalleyrailway.co.uk

GENERAL INFORMATION

Nearest Mainline Station: Braintree (7 miles)
Nearest Bus Station: Hedingham bus from
Braintree stops at the Railway (except on Sundays)
Car Parking: Parking at the site
Coach Parking: Free parking at site
Souvenir Shop(s): Yes
Food & Drinks: Yes – on operational days. Also
Pullman Sunday Lunches – bookings necessary.

SPECIAL INFORMATION

The railway is being re-built on a section of the old
Colne Valley & Halstead Railway, with all buildings,
bridges, signal boxes, etc. re-located on site.
The Railway also has a Farm Park to visit on site
(open between 2nd May and 4th October 2009).

OPERATING INFORMATION

Opening Times: 2010 dates: Trains run every
Sunday and Bank Holiday weekend from 28th
March to 3rd October. Open daily in August except
for Mondays and Fridays. Pre-booked parties any
time by arrangement and various other special
events. Please check the web site for further details.
Steam Working: Sundays 10.30pm to 4.00pm, Bank
Holidays from 10.30am to 4.00pm and 10.30am to
4.30pm on midweek operating days.
Prices: Adult – Steam days £8.00; Diesel £6.00
Child – Steam £5.00; Diesel £4.00
Family (2 adults + 4 children) –
Steam £28.00; Diesel £22.00
Senior Citizen – Steam £7.00; Diesel £5.00

Detailed Directions by Car:
The Railway is situated on the A1017 between Halstead and Haverhill, 7 miles north-west of Braintree.

THE DARTMOOR RAILWAY

Address: Okehampton Station, Station Road, Okehampton EX20 1EJ
Telephone Nº: (01837) 55164
Year Formed: 1997
Location of Line: Meldon Quarry to Coleford Junction

Length of Line: 15½ miles
Nº of Steam Locos: Visiting locos only
Nº of Other Locos: 1 and DMUs
Gauge: Standard
Web site: www.dartmoor-railway.co.uk

GENERAL INFORMATION

Nearest Mainline Station: Crediton
Nearest Bus Station: Okehampton
Car Parking: Okehampton Station and some spaces at Sampford Courtenay Station – all free of charge
Coach Parking: Okehampton Station
Souvenir Shop(s): Yes
Food & Drinks: Okehampton Buffet is open from Friday to Sunday throughout the year. The Buffet is fully licensed.

SPECIAL INFORMATION

The railway operates on the route of the old Southern Railway line through the mid-Devon countryside to the northern slopes of Dartmoor National Park.

OPERATING INFORMATION

Opening Times: Weekends and daily during the School Holidays from Easter until the end of September. Please contact the railway for details.
Steam Working: Visiting locomotives only. Please contact the railway for further information.
Prices: Vary depending upon the destination. Please contact the railway for further information.
Note: Commuter services through to Exeter are planned from 23rd May 2010.

Detailed Directions by Car:
From All Parts: Take the A30 Exeter to Launceston dual carriageway and exit at the Okehampton turn-off. Once in town, follow the brown tourist signs up the hill to Okehampton Station.

DEAN FOREST RAILWAY

Address: Norchard Centre, Forest Road; Lydney, Gloucestershire GL15 4ET **Telephone N°**: (01594) 845840 **Information Line**: (01594) 843423 (24 hr.) **Year Formed**: 1970 **Location of Line**: Lydney, Gloucestershire **Length of Line**: 4½ miles	**N° of Steam Locos**: 7 (4 working) **N° of Other Locos**: 18 **N° of Members**: 1,000 **Annual Membership Fee**: Adult £14.00; Family (4 persons) £17.00 **Approx N° of Visitors P.A.**: 35,000 **Gauge**: Standard **Web site**: www.deanforestrailway.co.uk

GENERAL INFORMATION

Nearest Mainline Station: Lydney (200 metres)
Nearest Bus Station: Lydney Town (400 metres)
Car Parking: 600 spaces available at Norchard
Coach Parking: Ample space available
Souvenir Shop(s): Yes + a Museum
Food & Drinks: Yes – on operational days only

SPECIAL INFORMATION

Dean Forest Railway preserves the sole surviving line of the Severn and Wye Railway. The Railway has lengthened the line to a total of 4½ miles and Norchard to Parkend is now open for steam train operation giving a round trip of 9 miles.

OPERATING INFORMATION

Opening Times: 2010 dates: Norchard is open every day for viewing. Trains operate on Sundays from March to the end of October, on Wednesdays and Saturdays from 4th June to 26th September, Thursdays in August and various other dates. Phone or check the railway's web site for further details.
Steam Working: Most services are steam-hauled – check the web site or phone for details. Trains depart Norchard at various times from 10.35am to 3.30pm.
Prices: Adult Return £10.00
Child Return £5.00 (ages 5-16 years old)
Family Tickets £28.00
Note: Fares may differ on Special Event days.

Detailed Directions by Car:
From M50 & Ross-on-Wye: Take the B4228 and B4234 via Coleford to reach Lydney. Norchard is located on the B4234, ¾ mile north of Lydney Town Centre; From Monmouth: Take the A4136 and B4431 onto the B4234 via Coleford; From South Wales: Take the M4 then M48 onto the A48 via Chepstow to Lydney; From Midlands/Gloucester: Take the M5 to Gloucester then the A48 to Lydney; From the West Country: Take the M4 and M48 via the 'Old' Severn Bridge to Chepstow and then the A48 to Lydney.

DERWENT VALLEY LIGHT RAILWAY

Address: Murton Park, Murton Lane, Murton, York   YO19 5UF
Telephone Nº: (01904) 489966
Year Formed: 1991
Location of Line: Murton, near York
Length of Line: ½ mile

Nº of Steam Locos: 2
Nº of Other Locos: 5
Nº of Members: 80
Annual Membership Fee: £10.00
Approx Nº of Visitors P.A.: 15,000
Gauge: Standard
Web site: www.dvlr.org.uk

GENERAL INFORMATION

Nearest Mainline Station: York (4 miles)
Nearest Bus Station: York (4 miles)
Car Parking: Large free car park at the site
Coach Parking: Free at the site
Souvenir Shop(s): Yes
Food & Drinks: Yes – as above

SPECIAL INFORMATION

The site is the remnants of the Derwent Valley Railway which was the last privately owned railway in England, originally opened in 1913.

OPERATING INFORMATION

Opening Times: Sundays and Bank Holidays from Easter until the end of September. Santa Specials also run during dates in December.
Steam Working: Second and last Sunday in the month and Bank Holidays – 10.30am to 4.15pm.
Prices: Adult £4.50
  Child £2.50
  Senior Citizens/Students £3.50
  Family Tickets £12.00 (2 adult + 4 child)
Prices are for entrance to the Yorkshire Museum of Farming – train rides are included in the price.

Detailed Directions by Car:
From All Parts: The railway is well signposted for the Yorkshire Museum of Farming from the A64 (York to Scarborough road), the A1079 (York to Hull road) and the A166 (York to Bridlington road).

DIDCOT RAILWAY CENTRE

Address: Didcot Railway Centre, Didcot, Oxfordshire OX11 7NJ
Telephone Nº: (01235) 817200
Year Formed: 1961
Location of Line: Didcot
Length of Line: ¾ mile
Gauge: Standard and 7 foot ¼ inch

Nº of Steam Locos: 23
Nº of Other Locos: 2
Nº of Members: 4,400
Annual Membership Fee: Full £26.00; Over 60/Under 18 £18.00; Family £33.00
Approx Nº of Visitors P.A.: 70,000
Web Site: www.didcotrailwaycentre.org.uk

GENERAL INFO

Nearest Mainline Station: Didcot Parkway (adjacent)
Nearest Bus Station: Buses to Didcot call at the Railway station
Car Parking: BR car park adjacent
Coach Parking: Further details on application
Souvenir Shop(s): Yes
Food & Drinks: Yes

SPECIAL INFO

The Centre is based on a Great Western Railway engine shed and is devoted to the re-creation of part of the GWR including Brunel's broad gauge railway and a newly built replica of the Fire Fly locomotive of 1840.

OPERATING INFO

Opening Times: 2010 dates: Weekends all year round, open daily during most school holidays and then from 1st June to 12th September. Weekends and Steam days open 10.30am to 5.00pm. Other days and during Winter open 10.30am to 4.00pm.
Steam Working: Bank Holidays and most weekends until 30th August. Wednesdays from 21st July to 25th August. Phone or check the web site for details of Autumn steam days.
Prices: Adult £5.00–£10.00
Child £4.00–£10.00
Discounted family tickets are often available (2 adults + 2 children). Prices vary depending on the events.

Detailed Directions by Car:
From East & West: Take the M4 to Junction 13 then the A34 and A4130 (follow brown Tourist signs to Didcot Railway Centre); From North: The Centre is signed from the A34 to A4130.

DOWNPATRICK & COUNTY DOWN RAILWAY

Address: Market Street, Downpatrick, Co. Down, Northern Ireland
Telephone Nº: (07790) 802049
Year Formed: 1985
Location of Line: Downpatrick
Length of Line: 2 miles
Gauge: Irish Standard (5 foot 3 inches)

Nº of Steam Locos: 3
Nº of Other Locos: 5
Nº of Members: 200
Annual Membership Fee: Adult £25.00, Family £50.00, Concessions £20.00
Approx Nº of Visitors P.A.: 13,000
Web: www.downrail.co.uk

GENERAL INFORMATION

Nearest Mainline Station: –
Nearest Bus Station: Adjacent to Station
Car Parking: Ample parking adjacent to Station
Coach Parking: Ample parking adjacent to Station
Souvenir Shop(s): Yes
Food & Drinks: Yes

SPECIAL INFORMATION

This is the only operating Standard (5' 3") Gauge Heritage Railway in Ireland.

OPERATING INFORMATION

Opening Times: The Museum is open daily from June to September.
Steam Working: 2010 dates: Weekends from June to September (includes August Bank Holiday). Trains are usually steam hauled and run from 2.00pm to 5.00pm. Special trains also run at Easter, Halloween and Christmas. Please contact the railway for further details.
Prices: Adult Return £5.00 (Single £3.00)
Child Return £4.00 (Single £2.50)

Detailed Directions by Car:
From Belfast take the A7 Downpatrick Road. Upon arrival in Downpatrick, follow the brown tourist signs and the Railway Museum is adjacent to the bus station.

EAST ANGLIAN RAILWAY MUSEUM

Address: Chappel & Wakes Colne Station, Colchester, Essex   CO6 2DS
Telephone Nº: (01206) 242524
Year Formed: 1969
Location of Line: 6 miles west of Colchester on Marks Tey to Sudbury branch
Length of Line: A third of a mile

Nº of Steam Locos: 5   **Other Locos**: 4
Nº of Members: 750
Annual Membership Fee: Adult £20.00; Senior Citizen £15.00
Approx Nº of Visitors P.A.: 40,000
Gauge: Standard
Web site: www.earm.co.uk

GENERAL INFORMATION

Nearest Mainline Station: Chappel & Wakes Colne (adajcent)
Nearest Bus Stop: Chappel (400 yards)
Car Parking: Free parking at site
Coach Parking: Free parking at site
Souvenir Shop(s): Yes
Food & Drinks: Yes – drinks are available every day and snacks are also available on operating days.

SPECIAL INFORMATION

The museum has the most comprehensive collection of railway architecture & engineering in the region. The railway also has a miniature railway that usually operates on steam days.

OPERATING INFORMATION

Opening Times: Open daily 10.00am to 4.30pm. Steam days open from 11.00am to 4.30pm. Closed on Christmas Day and Boxing Day.
Steam Working: Steam days are held every month from April to August and also in October and December. Bank Holidays are also Steam days. Check the web site for further details.
Prices: Adult £4.00 non-Steam; £8.00 Steam
Child £2.00 non-Steam; £4.00 Steam
O.A.P. £3.50 non-Steam; £7.00 Steam
Family £10.00 non-Steam; £20.00 Steam
Children under the age of 4 are admitted free of charge. A 10% discount is available for bookings for more than 10 people. A 10% discount is also available for visitors who visit using Mainline trains!

Detailed Directions by Car:
From North & South: Turn off the A12 south west of Colchester onto the A1124 (formerly the A604). The Museum is situated just off the A1124; From West: Turn off the A120 just before Marks Tey (signposted).

EAST KENT RAILWAY

Address: Station Road, Shepherdswell, Dover, Kent CT15 7PD **Telephone N°:** (01304) 832042 **Year Formed:** 1985 **Location of Line:** Between Shepherdswell and Eythorne **Length of Line:** 2 miles	**N° of Steam Locos:** 1 **N° of Other Locos:** 7 + 2 DMUs **N° of Members:** 400 **Annual Membership Fee:** £15.00 (Adult) **Approx N° of Visitors P.A.:** 4,500 **Gauge:** Standard and also 5 inch and 3¼ inch miniature gauges **Web site:** www.eastkentrailway.co.uk

GENERAL INFORMATION

Nearest Mainline Station: Shepherdswell (50 yards)
Car Parking: Available Shepherdswell and Eythorne
Coach Parking: In adjacent Station Yard
Souvenir Shop(s): Yes
Food & Drinks: Yes

SPECIAL INFORMATION

The East Kent Railway was originally built between 1911 and 1917 to service Tilmanstone Colliery. Closed in the mid-1980's, the railway was re-opened in 1995.

OPERATING INFORMATION

Opening Times: The 2010 operating season has a special 'Travel for a Pound' day on 21st March and then runs from 2nd April until 19th September. Trains run every Sunday and Bank Holiday during this period plus Saturdays in August and during some special events including Halloween and Santa Specials. Contact the railway for further details.
Steam Working: None at present.
Prices: Adult £7.00
　　　　 Child £4.00
　　　　 Senior Citizens £6.00
　　　　 Family £17.00 (2 Adults and 2 Children)

Detailed Directions by Car:
From the A2: Take the turning to Shepherdswell and continue to the village. Pass the shop on the left and cross the railway bridge. Take the next left (Station Road) signposted at the traffic lights for the EKR; From the A256: Take the turning for Eythorne at the roundabout on the section between Eastry and Whitfield. Follow the road through Eythorne. Further on you will cross the railway line and enter Shepherdswell. After a few hundred yards take the right turn signposted for the EKR.

EAST LANCASHIRE RAILWAY

Address: Bolton Street Station, Bury, Lancashire BL9 0EY
Telephone Nº: (0161) 764-7790
Year Formed: 1968
Location of Line: Heywood, Bury and Rawtenstall
Length of Line: 12 miles

Nº of Steam Locos: 14
Nº of Other Locos: 16
Nº of Members: 4,500
Annual Membership Fee: £19.00
Approx Nº of Visitors P.A.: 110,000
Gauge: Standard
Web site: www.east-lancs-rly.co.uk

GENERAL INFORMATION

Nearest Mainline Station: Manchester (then Metro Link to Bury)
Nearest Bus Station: ¼ mile
Car Parking: Adjacent
Coach Parking: Adjacent
Souvenir Shop(s): Yes
Food & Drinks: Yes

SPECIAL INFORMATION

Originally opened in 1846, the East Lancashire Railway was re-opened in 1987.

OPERATING INFORMATION

Opening Times: Every weekend & Bank Holiday 9.00am to 5.00pm. Also Wednesday to Friday from May to mid-September. A number of special events also run throughout the year.
Steam Working: Most trains are steam-hauled. Saturdays alternate Steam & Diesel. 2 engines in steam on Sundays.
Prices: Adult Return £12.20
　　　　　　Child Return £8.20
　　　　　　Family Return £32.50
Cheaper fares are available for shorter journeys.

Detailed Directions by Car:
From All Parts: Exit the M66 at Junction 2 and take the A56 into Bury. Follow the brown tourist signs and turn right into Bolton Street at the junction with the A58. The station is about 150 yards on the right.

EAST SOMERSET RAILWAY (STRAWBERRY LINE)

Address: Cranmore Railway Station, Shepton Mallet, Somerset BA4 4QP
Telephone Nº: (01749) 880417
Year Formed: 1971
Location of Line: Cranmore, off A361 between Frome and Shepton Mallet
Length of Line: 3 miles

Nº of Steam Locos: 5
Nº of Other Locos: 2
Nº of Members: 480
Annual Season Ticket Fee: Single £30.00
Family £80.00
Approx Nº of Visitors P.A.: 20,000
Gauge: Standard

GENERAL INFORMATION

Nearest Mainline Station: Castle Cary (10 miles)
Nearest Bus Station: Shepton Mallet (3 miles)
Car Parking: Space for 100 cars available
Coach Parking: Available by arrangement
Souvenir Shop(s): Yes
Food & Drinks: Yes

SPECIAL INFORMATION

Footplate experience courses available – phone (01749) 880417 for further details.

Web site: www.eastsomersetrailway.com

OPERATING INFORMATION

Opening Times: Complex, Museum and Engine Sheds open daily from April to December and Tuesdays, Thursdays, Saturdays, January to March. Closed on Mondays and Wednesdays in November.
Steam Working: 2010 dates: Weekends and Bank Holidays from 3rd April to September, Wednesdays from June to August and Thursdays in August. Santa Specials run on some December weekends. Special events on other dates. Open 10.00am to 4.00pm (5.30pm in the Summer).
Prices: Adult Return £7.50   Child Return £5.50
Senior Citizen Return £6.50   Family Return £22.00

Detailed Directions by Car:
From the North: Take A367/A37 to Shepton Mallet then turn left onto A361 to Frome. Carry on to Shepton Mallet and 9 miles after Frome turn left at Cranmore; From the South: Take A36 to Frome bypass then A361 to Cranmore; From the West: Take A371 from Wells to Shepton Mallet, then A361 to Frome (then as above).

Ecclesbourne Valley Railway

Address: Station Road, Coldwell Street, Wirksworth DE4 4FB	**Nº of Steam Locos:** 3
Telephone Nº: (01629) 823076	**Nº of Other Locos:** 9
Year Formed: 2000	**Nº of Members:** 600+
Location of Line: Wirksworth to Duffield	**Annual Membership Fee:** £12.00
Length of Line: 4 miles	**Approx Nº of Visitors P.A.:** 15,000
	Gauge: Standard
	Web site: www.e-v-r.com

GENERAL INFORMATION

Nearest Mainline Station: Cromford (2 miles)
Nearest Bus Station: Derby (13 miles)
Car Parking: Available at the Station
Coach Parking: Available at the Station
Souvenir Shop(s): Yes
Food & Drinks: Yes

SPECIAL INFORMATION

The line is currently being restored section by section and the Railway now hopes to complete all 8½ miles by 2011.

OPERATING INFORMATION

Opening Times: 2010 dates: Wirksworth to Ravenstor and Idridgehay on weekends and Bank Holidays from 20th March to 31st October. Trains also run from Wirksworth to Ravenstor on Tuesdays, Wednesdays and Thursdays from 27th July to 2nd September. Services usually run from around 11.20am until 3.45pm though times vary. Please contact the railway for further details.
Steam Working: To be introduced in August 2010
Prices: Adult Day Rover £3.50 to £10.00
Child Day Rover £2.00 to £5.00
Concessions Day Rover £3.00 to £9.00
Family Day Rover £10.00 to £18.00
Note: Prices vary depending on journey length.

Detailed Directions by Car:
From All Parts: Exit the M1 at Junction 26 and take the A610 Ambergate then the A6 to Whatstandwell. Turn left onto the B5035 to Wirksworth and the station is at the bottom of the hill as you enter the town.

ELSECAR HERITAGE RAILWAY

Address: Wath Road, Elsecar, Barnsley, S74 8HJ **Telephone Nº**: (01226) 746746 **Year Formed**: 2002 **Location of Line**: Elsecar, near Barnsley **Length of Line**: 1 mile	**Nº of Steam Locos**: 2 **Nº of Other Locos**: 3 **Nº of Members**: Approximately 64 **Annual Membership Fee**: £10.00 **Approx Nº of Visitors P.A.**: 20,000 **Gauge**: Standard **Web site**: www.elsecarrailway.cjb.net

GENERAL INFORMATION

Nearest Mainline Station: Elsecar
Nearest Bus Station: Barnsley
Car Parking: Large free car park at the site
Coach Parking: At the site
Souvenir Shop(s): Yes
Food & Drinks: Yes

SPECIAL INFORMATION

The Railway is based at the Elsecar Heritage Centre which is an antiques and craft centre with a wide range of displays and special events.

OPERATING INFORMATION

Opening Times: The Heritage Centre is open daily from 10.00am to 5.00pm throughout the year (but closed between 25th December and 2nd January). Trains run on Sundays, Bank Holidays and during Special Events throughout the year plus Wednesdays in August. Hourly services from 12.00pm to 4.00pm.
Steam Working: Most services are diesel-hauled with occasional steaming during the Summer months. Please phone for further details.
Prices: Adults £3.50   Children £2.00
             Senior Citizens £2.50
Admission to the site is free of charge except for during Special Events.

Detailed Directions by Car:
From All Parts: Exit the M1 at Junction 36 and follow the brown 'Elsecar Heritage' signs taking the A6135 for approximately 2 miles. Turn left onto Broad Carr Road for just under a mile, then right onto Armroyd Lane and right again onto Fitzwilliam Street. Free visitor car parking is available on Wentworth Road off the junction of Fitzwilliam Street and Wath Road.

EMBSAY & BOLTON ABBEY STEAM RAILWAY

Address: Bolton Abbey Station, Bolton Abbey, Skipton, N. Yorkshire BD23 6AF
Telephone Nº: (01756) 710614
Year Formed: 1968
Location of Line: 2 miles east of Skipton
Length of Line: 4½ miles

Nº of Steam Locos: 19
Nº of Other Locos: 12
Nº of Members: 700
Annual Membership Fee: £15.00
Approx Nº of Visitors P.A.: 107,000
Gauge: Standard

GENERAL INFORMATION

Nearest Mainline Station: Skipton (2 miles), Ilkley (3 miles)
Nearest Bus Station: Skipton (2 miles), Ilkley (3 mls)
Car Parking: Large car park at both Stations
Coach Parking: Large coach park at both Stations
Souvenir Shop(s): Yes
Food & Drinks: Yes – Cafe + Buffet cars

SPECIAL INFORMATION

The line extension to Bolton Abbey opened in 1998.

Web site: www.embsayboltonabbeyrailway.org.uk

OPERATING INFORMATION

Opening Times: Every Sunday throughout the year. Weekends from Easter to the end of October and daily in the summer season until early September. Tuesdays in May and September. Santa Specials run on December weekends.
Steam Working: Steam trains depart Embsay Station at 10.30am, 12.00pm, 1.30pm, 3.00pm and 4.30pm on most days during the Main Season. Contact the railway for further details.
Prices: Adult Return £8.00   Child Return £4.00
Concessionary Return £7.00
Family Ticket £20.00 (2 adult + 2 children)
Different fares may apply on special event days.

Detailed Directions by Car:
From All Parts: Embsay Station is off the A59 Skipton bypass by the Harrogate Road. Bolton Abbey Station is off the A59 at Bolton Abbey.

FOXFIELD STEAM RAILWAY

Address: Caverswall Road Station, Blythe Bridge, Stoke-on-Trent, Staffs. ST11 9EA
Telephone Nº: (01782) 396210
Year Formed: 1967
Location of Line: Blythe Bridge
Length of Line: 3½ miles
Gauge: Standard

Nº of Steam Locos: 22
Nº of Other Locos: 15
Nº of Members: Over 300
Annual Membership Fee: Adult £12.00; Junior £6.00; Family £20.00
Approx Nº of Visitors P.A.: 25,000
Web site: www.foxfieldrailway.co.uk

GENERAL INFORMATION

Nearest Mainline Station: Blythe Bridge (¼ mile)
Nearest Bus Station: Hanley (5 miles)
Car Parking: Space for 300 cars available
Coach Parking: Space for 6 coaches available
Souvenir Shop(s): Yes
Food & Drinks: Yes – Buffet and Real Ale Bar

SPECIAL INFORMATION

The Railway is a former Colliery railway built in 1893 to take coal from Foxfield Colliery. It has the steepest Standard Gauge adhesion worked gradient in the UK and freight trains can be seen on these gradients during the annual Steam Gala in July.

OPERATING INFORMATION

Opening Times: Sundays & Bank Holiday Mondays from Easter to the end of October. Also weekends in December. Open 11.00am to 5.00pm.
Steam Working: 11.30am, 1.00pm, 2.30pm and 4.00pm although Special Event days also run trains at earlier times.
Prices: Adult Tickets – £7.50
Child Tickets – £3.00 (3-16 years old)
Senior Citizen Tickets – £5.50
Fares may vary on special event days.

Detailed Directions by Car:
From South: Exit M6 at Junction 14 onto the A34 to Stone then the A520 to Meir and the A50 to Blythe Bridge; From North: Exit M6 at Junction 15 then the A500 to Stoke-on-Trent and the A50 to Blythe Bridge; From East: Take the A50 to Blythe Bridge. Once in Blythe Bridge, turn by the Mainline crossing.

GLOUCESTERSHIRE WARWICKSHIRE RAILWAY

Address: The Station, Toddington, Cheltenham, Gloucestershire GL54 5DT
Telephone Nº: (01242) 621405
Year Formed: 1981
Location of Line: 5 miles south of Broadway, Worcestershire, near the A46
Length of Line: 10 miles

Nº of Steam Locos: 11
Nº of Other Locos: 17
Nº of Members: 3,500
Annual Membership Fee: £16.00 (Adult)
Approx Nº of Visitors P.A.: 70,000
Gauge: Standard and Narrow gauge
Web site: www.gwsr.com

GENERAL INFORMATION

Nearest Mainline Station: Cheltenham Spa or Ashchurch
Nearest Bus Station: Cheltenham
Car Parking: Parking available at Toddington, Winchcombe & Cheltenham Racecourse Stations
Coach Parking: Parking available as above
Souvenir Shop(s): Yes
Food & Drinks: Yes

SPECIAL INFORMATION

The North Gloucestershire narrow gauge railway also runs from Toddington Station. Gotherington Halt is now open on the off-peak timetable with access by foot only.

OPERATING INFORMATION

Opening Times: Weekends and Bank Holidays from March to December. Also during selected weekdays – please contact the railway for further details. Trains run from 10.30am to 5.00pm
Steam Working: Most operating days
Prices: Adult Return £11.00
Child Return £6.50
Senior Citizen Return £9.50
Family Return £30.00 (2 Adult + 3 Child)
Under 5's travel free of charge apart from on some Special Event days.

Detailed Directions by Car:
Toddington is 11 miles north east of Cheltenham, 5 miles south of Broadway just off the B4632 (old A46). Exit the M5 at Junction 9 towards Stow-on-the-Wold for the B4632. The Railway is clearly visible from the B4632.

GREAT CENTRAL RAILWAY

Address: Great Central Station, Great Central Road, Loughborough, Leicestershire LE11 1RW **Telephone Nº:** (01509) 230726 **Year Formed:** 1969 **Location of Line:** From Loughborough to Leicester	**Length of Line:** 8 miles **Nº of Steam Locos:** 10 **Nº of Other Locos:** 11 **Nº of Members:** 5,000 **Annual Membership Fee:** £25.00 **Approx Nº of Visitors P.A.:** 150,000 **Gauge:** Standard

GENERAL INFORMATION

Nearest Mainline Station: Loughborough (1 mile)
Nearest Bus Station: Loughborough (½ mile)
Car Parking: Street parking outside the Station
Coach Parking: Car parks at Quorn & Woodhouse, Rothley and Leicester North
Souvenir Shop(s): Yes
Food & Drinks: Yes – Buffet or Restaurant cars are usually available for snacks or other meals

Web site: www.gcrailway.co.uk

SPECIAL INFORMATION

The aim of the GCR is to recreate the experience of British main line railway operation during the best years of steam locomotives.

OPERATING INFORMATION

Opening Times: 2010 dates: Weekends throughout the year, most Wednesdays in July then Tuesday to Thursday 20th July to 2nd September. Santa Specials in December.
Steam Working: Weekends, Bank Holidays and some Special Events throughout the year.
Prices: Adult Day ticket £14.00
Child Day ticket £9.00
Senior Citizen Day ticket £12.00
Family Day Ticket £32 (2 adults + 3 children)

Detailed Directions by Car:
Great Central Road is on the South East side of Loughborough and is clearly signposted from the A6 Leicester Road and A60 Nottingham Road.

GREAT CENTRAL RAILWAY (NOTTINGHAM)

Address: Nottingham Transport Heritage Centre, Mere Way, Ruddington, Nottingham   NG11 6NX
Telephone Nº: (0115) 940-5705
Fax Nº: (0115) 940-5905
Year Formed: 1990 (Opened in 1994)
Location of Line: Ruddington to Loughborough Junction

Length of Line: 9 miles
Nº of Steam Locos: 6
Nº of Other Locos: 10
Nº of Members: 750
Annual Membership Fee: £14.00
Approx Nº of Visitors P.A.: 15,000
Gauge: Standard
Web site: www.nthc.co.uk

GENERAL INFORMATION

Nearest Mainline Station: Nottingham (5 miles)
Nearest Bus Station: Bus service from Nottingham to Ruddington
Car Parking: Free parking at site
Coach Parking: Free parking at site
Souvenir Shop(s): Yes
Food & Drinks: Yes

SPECIAL INFORMATION

The Heritage Centre covers an area of over eleven acres and is set within the Rushcliffe Country Park in Ruddington. Trains run to Loughborough Junction or Rushcliffe Halt.

OPERATING INFORMATION

Opening Times: Sundays and Bank Holidays plus some Saturdays from Easter until October. Open 10.45am to 5.00pm. Also open for Santa Specials on December weekends.
Steam Working: Steam service runs from 11.30am
Prices: Adult   £6.50 – £8.00
              Child   £3.50 – £4.00
              Senior Citizens £5.50 – £7.00
              Family £18.50 – £22.00
                  (2 adults + 2 children)
Note: Prices vary depending on the journey length.

Detailed Directions by Car:
From All Parts: The centre is situated off the A60 Nottingham to Loughborough Road and is signposted just south of the traffic lights at Ruddington.

GWILI RAILWAY

Address: Bronwydd Arms Station, Bronwydd Arms, Carmarthen SA33 6HT
Telephone Nº: (01267) 238213
Year Formed: 1975
Location of Line: Near Carmarthen, South Wales
Length of Line: 2½ miles

Nº of Steam Locos: 5
Nº of Other Locos: 6
Nº of Members: 900 shareholders, 450 Society members
Annual Membership Fee: £15.00
Approx Nº of Visitors P.A.: 24,000
Gauge: Standard
Web site: www.gwili-railway.co.uk

GENERAL INFORMATION

Nearest Mainline Station:
Carmarthen (3 miles)
Nearest Bus Station:
Carmarthen (3 miles)
Car Parking: Free parking at Bronwydd Arms except for a few special occasions
Coach Parking:
Free parking at Bronwydd Arms
Souvenir Shop(s): Yes
Food & Drinks: Yes

SPECIAL INFORMATION

Gwili Railway was the first Standard Gauge preserved railway in Wales. There is a riverside picnic area and Miniature railway at Llwyfan Cerrig Station and there is a Signal Box Museum at the Bronwydd Arms.

OPERATING INFO

Opening Times: Bank Holidays from April, some other dates in May then Wednesdays and Sundays in June and July. Daily in August except for Saturdays. Open most weekends in September and December. Also open on certain other dates. Please phone or check the website for further details.
Steam Working: All advertised trains are steam hauled. Trains run from 10.30am to 4.10pm in high season and 11.15am to 3.45pm at other times.
Prices: Adult £6.00
Child £3.00
Family £15.00
(2 adults + up to 2 children)
Senior Citizens £5.00
Note: Discounts are available for groups of 10 or more.

Detailed Directions by Car:
The Railway is three miles North of Carmarthen – signposted off the A484 Carmarthen to Cardigan Road.

HEAD OF STEAM – DARLINGTON RAILWAY MUSEUM

Address: North Road Station, Darlington, Co. Durham   DL3 6ST
Telephone Nº: (01325) 460532
Year Formed: 1975
Location of Line: Adjacent to North Road Station
Length of Line: ¼ mile

Nº of Steam Locos: 4
Nº of Other Locos: –
Nº of Members: 800 family memberships
Annual Membership Fee: £12.00 (adult) £15.00 (family);   £10.00 (senior)
Approx Nº of Visitors P.A.: 33,500
Gauge: Standard
Web site: www.head-of-steam.co.uk

GENERAL INFORMATION

Nearest Mainline Station: North Road (adjacent)
Nearest Bus Station: Darlington (1 mile)
Car Parking: Free parking at site
Coach Parking: Free parking at site
Souvenir Shop(s): Yes
Food & Drinks: Cafe open 11.00am to 2.00pm (until 3.00pm at weekends).

SPECIAL INFORMATION

The museum is an 1842 station on the route of the Stockton and Darlington Railway and is devoted to the Railways of north-east England.

OPERATING INFORMATION

Opening Times: The Museum is open daily throughout the year but is closed every Monday. from April to September and every Monday and Thursday from October to March. Also closed on Christmas Day, Boxing Day and New Year's Day. Open 10.00am to 4.00pm April to September and from 11.00am to 3.30pm from October to March.
Steam Working: At various Special events throughout the year – please phone for details.
Prices: Adult £4.95
Child £3.00 (ages 5 and under enter free)
Senior Citizen £3.75
Family Ticket £10.00
(2 adults and up to 4 children)

Detailed Directions by Car:
From Darlington Town Centre: Follow the A167 north for about ¾ mile then turn left immediately before the Railway bridge; From A1(M): Exit at Junction 59 then follow A167 towards Darlington and turn right after passing under the Railway bridge.

HOLLYCOMBE STEAM COLLECTION

Address: Hollycombe, Liphook, Hants. GU30 7LP **Telephone Nº**: (01428) 724900 **Year Formed**: 1970 **Location of Line**: Hollycombe, Liphook **Length of Line**: 1¾ miles Narrow gauge, ¼ mile Standard gauge	**Nº of Steam Locos**: 6 **Nº of Other Locos**: 2 **Nº of Members**: 100 **Annual Membership Fee**: £8.00 **Approx Nº of Visitors P.A.**: 35,000 **Gauge**: 2 feet plus Standard & 7¼ inches **Web site**: www.hollycombe.co.uk

GENERAL INFORMATION

Nearest Mainline Station: Liphook (1 mile)
Nearest Bus Station: Liphook
Car Parking: Extensive grass area
Coach Parking: Hardstanding
Souvenir Shop(s): Yes
Food & Drinks: Yes – Cafe

SPECIAL INFORMATION

The narrow gauge railway ascends to spectacular views of the Downs and is part of an extensive working steam museum.

OPERATING INFORMATION

Opening Times: 2010 dates: Sundays and Bank Holidays from Easter until the 24th October. Also open Tuesday to Friday in August.
Steam Working: The Standard Gauge steam weekend is held at the start of June 2010 and features a Belgian vertical boiler tank Locomotive. Please contact the railway for further information.
Prices: Adult £11.00
　　　　　Child £9.00
　　　　　Senior Citizen £9.00
　　　　　Family £35.00 (2 adults + 3 children)

Detailed Directions by Car:
Take the A3 to Liphook and follow the brown tourist signs for the railway.

ISLE OF WIGHT STEAM RAILWAY

Address: The Railway Station, Haven Street, Ryde, Isle of Wight PO33 4DS	**Nº of Other Locos**: 3
Telephone Nº: (01983) 882204	**Nº of Members**: 1,300
Year Formed: 1971 (re-opened)	**Annual Membership Fee**: £20.00
Location: Smallbrook Junction to Wootton	**Approx Nº of Visitors P.A.**: 100,000
Length of Line: 5 miles	**Gauge**: Standard
Nº of Steam Locos: 11	**Talking Timetable**: (01983) 884343
	Web site: www.iwsteamrailway.co.uk

GENERAL INFORMATION

Nearest Mainline Station: Smallbrook Junction (direct interchange)
Nearest Bus: From Ryde & Newport direct
Car Parking: Free parking at Havenstreet & Wootton Stations
Coach Parking: Free at Havenstreet Station
Souvenir Shop(s): Yes – at Havenstreet Station
Food & Drinks: Yes – at Havenstreet Station

SPECIAL INFORMATION

The IWSR uses mostly Victorian & Edwardian locomotives and carriages to recreate the atmosphere of an Isle of Wight branch line railway.

OPERATING INFORMATION

Opening Times: Selected dates between March and December and also daily from mid-June to mid-September. Please contact the railway for further information.
Steam Working: 10.30am to 4.00pm (depending on the Station)
Prices: Adult Return £9.00
Child Return £5.00
Family Return £24.00
(2 adults + 2 children)

Detailed Directions by Car:
To reach the Isle of Wight head for the Ferry ports at Lymington, Southampton or Portsmouth. From all parts of the Isle of Wight, head for Ryde and follow the brown tourist signs.

KEIGHLEY & WORTH VALLEY RAILWAY

Address: The Station, Haworth, Keighley, West Yorkshire   BD22 8NJ
Telephone Nº: (01535) 645214 (enquiries); (01535) 647777 (24 hour timetable)
Year Formed: 1962 (Line re-opened 1968)
Location of Line: From Keighley southwards through Haworth to Oxenhope
Length of Line: 4¾ miles

Nº of Steam Locos: 30
Nº of Other Locos: 10
Members: 4,500 (350 working members)
Annual Membership Fee: Adult £18.00; Adult life membership £360.00
Approx Nº of Visitors P.A.: 150,000
Gauge: Standard
Web Site: www.kwvr.co.uk

GENERAL INFORMATION

Nearest Mainline Station: Keighley (adjacent)
Nearest Bus Station: Keighley (5 minutes walk)
Car Parking: Parking at Keighley, Ingrow, Haworth (charged) and Oxenhope
Coach Parking: At Ingrow & Oxenhope (phone in advance)
Souvenir Shop(s): Yes – at Keighley, Haworth & Oxenhope
Food & Drinks: Yes – at Keighley & Oxenhope when trains run.

OPERATING INFORMATION

Opening Times: 2010 dates: Weekends & Bank Holidays throughout the year. Daily from 26th June to 5th September. Also open during Easter, Whit and October School holidays and from 26th to 31st December.
Steam Working: Early trains are Diesel; Steam runs from mid-morning on all operating days (except 4 weekends prior to Christmas).
Prices: Adult Return £9.40; £14.00 day rover
Child Return £4.70; £7.00 day rover
Family Return £23.50 (2 adults, 3 children)
Family Day Rover £33.00

Detailed Directions by Car:
Exit the M62 at Junction 26 and take the M606 to its' end. Follow the ring-road signs around Bradford to Shipley. Take the A650 through Bingley to Keighley and follow the brown tourist signs to the railway. Alternatively, take the A6033 from Hebden Bridge to Oxenhope and follow the brown signs to Oxenhope or Haworth Stations.

THE KEITH & DUFFTOWN RAILWAY

Address: Dufftown Station, Dufftown, Banffshire, AB55 4BA **Telephone Nº**: (01340) 821181 **Year Formed**: 2000 **Location of Line**: Keith to Dufftown **Length of Line**: 11 miles	**Nº of Steam Locos**: None at present **Nº of Other Locos**: 2 **Nº of Members**: Approximately 400 **Annual Membership Fee**: Adult £11.00 **Approx Nº of Visitors P.A.**: Not known **Gauge**: Standard **Web site**: www.keith-dufftown-railway.co.uk

GENERAL INFORMATION

Nearest Mainline Station: Keith (½ mile)
Nearest Bus Station: Elgin (Bus routes travel to both Keith and Dufftown)
Car Parking: Available at both Stations
Coach Parking: Available at both Stations
Souvenir Shop(s): Yes – at Keith Town Station
Food & Drinks: Available at Dufftown Station

SPECIAL INFORMATION

The Keith and Dufftown Railway is an eleven mile line linking the World's Malt Whisky Capital, Dufftown, to the market town of Keith. The line, which was reopened by volunteers during 2000 and 2001, passes through some of Scotland's most picturesque scenery, with forest and farmland, lochs and glens, castles and distilleries.

OPERATING INFORMATION

Opening Times: Weekends from Easter until the end of September and also on Fridays in June, July and August. Trains depart Dufftown from 11.25am until 3.50pm.
Steam Working: None at present
Prices: Adult Return £9.50
        Child Return £4.50
        Senior Citizen Return £7.50
        Family Return £23.00
Note: Shorter journeys are cheaper.

Detailed Directions by Car:
Keith Town Station is located in Keith, on the A96 Aberdeen to Inverness Road; Dufftown Station is about 1 mile to the north of the Dufftown Town Centre just off the A941 road to Elgin.

Kent & East Sussex Railway

Address: Tenterden Town Station, Tenterden, Kent   TN30 6HE
Telephone Nº: (01580) 765155
Year Formed: 1974
Location of Line: Tenterden, Kent to Bodiam, East Sussex
Length of Line: 10½ miles

Nº of Steam Locos: 12
Nº of Other Locos: 6
Nº of Members: 2,100
Annual Membership Fee: £23.00
Approx Nº of Visitors P.A.: 99,000
Gauge: Standard
Web site: www.kesr.org.uk

GENERAL INFORMATION

Nearest Mainline Station: Headcorn (8 miles)
Nearest Bus Station: Tenterden
Car Parking: Free parking available at Tenterden Town and Northiam Stations
Coach Parking: Tenterden & Northiam
Souvenir Shop(s): Yes
Food & Drinks: Yes

SPECIAL INFORMATION

Built as Britain's first light railway, the K&ESR opened in 1900 and was epitomised by sharp curved and steep gradients and to this day retains a charm and atmosphere all of its own.

OPERATING INFORMATION

Opening Times: From March to October and in December. The return journey time is 1 hour 55 minutes. Please phone the 24 hour talking-timetable for precise operating information: (01580) 762943
Steam Working: Every operational day
Prices: Adult Ticket – £12.80
Child Ticket – £7.80
Senior Citizen Ticket – £11.80
Family Ticket – £34.00
(2 adults + 3 children or 1 adult + 4 children)
Note: The prices shown above are for Day Rover tickets which allow unlimited travel on the day of purchase.

Detailed Directions by Car:
From London and Kent Coast: Travel to Ashford (M20) then take the A28 to Tenterden; From Sussex Coast: Take A28 from Hastings to Northiam.

LAKESIDE & HAVERTHWAITE RAILWAY

Address: Haverthwaite Station, near Ulverston, Cumbria LA12 8AL
Telephone Nº: (015395) 31594
Year Formed: 1973
Location of Line: Haverthwaite to Lakeside
Length of Line: 3½ miles

Nº of Steam Locos: 8
Nº of Other Locos: 6
Nº of Members: 250
Annual Membership Fee: £12.00 Adult, £6.00 Juniors
Approx Nº of Visitors P.A.: 170,000
Gauge: Standard
Web site: www.lakesiderailway.co.uk

GENERAL INFORMATION

Nearest Mainline Station: Ulverston (7 miles)
Nearest Bus Station: Haverthwaite (100 yards)
Car Parking: Plenty of spaces – £1.50 charge
Coach Parking: Free parking at site
Souvenir Shop(s): Yes
Food & Drinks: Yes

SPECIAL INFORMATION

Tickets which include train ride followed by a cruise on Lake Windermere or a visit to the Aquarium of the Lakes are also available from the Railway.

OPERATING INFORMATION

Opening Times: 2010 dates: Daily from 27th March to 31st October inclusive. Santa Specials run on weekends in December (but not on 24th and 25th). Also Thomas the Tank Engine weekends on 20th and 21st March and 6th and 7th November.
Steam Working: Daily from morning to late afternoon.
Prices:

Adult Return £5.90	Single £3.55
Child Return £2.95	Single £2.40
Family Ticket £15.50	

Note: Prices vary for Special Events.

Detailed Directions by Car:
From All Parts: Exit the M6 at Junction 36 and follow the brown tourist signs.

THE LAVENDER LINE

Address: Isfield Station, Isfield, near Uckfield, East Sussex TN22 5XB	**N⁰ of Steam Locos:** 1
Telephone N⁰: (01825) 750515	**N⁰ of Other Locos:** 3 + DEMU
Year Formed: 1992	**N⁰ of Members:** Approximately 400
Location of Line: East Sussex between Lewes and Uckfield	**Annual Membership Fee:** £15.00
	Approx N⁰ of Visitors P.A.: 12,500
Length of Line: 1 mile	**Gauge:** Standard
	Web site: www.lavender-line.co.uk

GENERAL INFORMATION

Nearest Mainline Station: Uckfield (3 miles)
Nearest Bus Station: Uckfield (3 miles)
Car Parking: Free parking at site
Coach Parking: Can cater for coach parties – please contact the Railway.
Souvenir Shop: Yes
Food & Drinks: Yes – Cinders Buffet

SPECIAL INFORMATION

Isfield Station has been restored as a Southern Railway country station complete with the original L.B.S.C.R. signalbox.

OPERATING INFORMATION

Opening Times: Sundays throughout the year. Some Weekends in June, July and August plus Wednesdays and Thursdays in August. Also open on Bank Holidays, daily during February and October School half-term holidays and for Santa Specials in December.
Steam Working: Please phone for details.
Prices: Adult £8.00
　　　　 Child £5.00
　　　　 Senior Citizen £7.00
　　　　 Family Ticket £26.00
　　　　 (2 adults + 3 children)
All tickets offer unlimited rides on the day of issue and prices may vary on special event days.

Detailed Directions by Car::
From All Parts: Isfield is just off the A26 midway between Lewes and Uckfield.

LINCOLNSHIRE WOLDS RAILWAY

Address: The Railway Station, Ludborough, Lincolnshire DN36 5SQ
Telephone Nº: (01507) 363881
Year Formed: 1979
Location of Line: Ludborough – off the A16(T) between Grimsby and Louth
Length of Line: 1½ miles

Nº of Steam Locos: 3   **Other Locos**: 7
Nº of Members of the Supporting Society (LWRS): 400+
Annual Membership Fee: £26.00 Family, £13.00 Adult, £8.00 Senior Citizen
Approx Nº of Visitors P.A.: 9,000
Gauge: Standard

Photo courtesy of B. Wakefield

GENERAL INFORMATION

Nearest Mainline Station: Grimsby (8 miles)
Nearest Bus Stop: Ludborough (½ mile)
Car Parking: Available at Ludborough Station only
Coach Parking: Space for 1 coach only
Souvenir Shop(s): Yes
Food & Drinks: Yes

SPECIAL INFORMATION

The buildings and facilities at Ludborough have been completed and short steam trips commenced in 1998. A line extension to North Thoresby (1½ miles) is now open.

OPERATING INFORMATION

Opening Times: Certain Sundays from January to December, Wednesdays in August and Santa Specials in December. Please note that advance bookings are essential for Santa Specials.
Steam Working: Contact the Railway for details.
Prices: Adults £6.00   Children £3.00
Senior Citizens £4.00
Family £15.00 (2 adults + 4 children)
Different fares may apply at Special Events.
Prices include unlimited rides throughout the day.

Web site: www.lincolnshirewoldsrailway.co.uk

Detailed Directions by Car:
The Railway is situated near Ludborough, ½ mile off the A16(T) Louth to Grimsby road. Follow signs to Fulstow to reach the station (approximately ½ mile). Do not turn into Ludborough but stay on the bypass.

Llangollen Railway

Address: The Station, Abbey Road, Llangollen, Denbighshire LL20 8SN **Telephone No**: (01978) 860979 **Year Formed**: 1975 **Location of Line**: Valley of the River Dee from Llangollen to Carrog **Length of Line**: 7½ miles	**No of Steam Locos**: 14 **No of Other Locos**: 13 **No of Members**: 1,400 **Annual Membership Fee**: Adult £18.00; Family £25.00; Junior (under-16) £10.00 **Approx No of Visitors P.A.**: 110,000 **Gauge**: Standard

GENERAL INFORMATION

Nearest Mainline Station: Ruabon (6 miles)
Nearest Bus Station: Wrexham (12 miles)
Car Parking: Public car park at Lower Dee Mill off A539 Ruabon road.
Coach Parking: Market Street car park in town centre
Souvenir Shop(s): Yes – at Llangollen Station
Food & Drinks: Yes – at Llangollen, Berwyn, Glyndyfrdwy and Carrog Stations.

SPECIAL INFORMATION

The route originally formed part of the line from Ruabon to Barmouth Junction, closed in 1964. The railway has been rebuilt by volunteers since 1975, reopening to Carrog in 1996.
The ultimate aim is to reopen to Corwen (10 miles).

OPERATING INFORMATION

Opening Times: 2010 dates: Services run daily from 26th March to 17th October. Also on weekends in December, other Santa Specials near Christmas and a number of other dates throughout the year including most days in April and School Holidays.
Steam Working: Phone the Talking timetable number for further details: (01978) 860951
Prices: Adult Day Rover £10.00
Child Day Rover £5.00
Family Day Rover £22.00 (2 adult + 2 child)
Senior Citizen Day Rover £8.00
Note: Tickets for shorter journeys are cheaper.

Web Site: www.llangollen-railway.co.uk

Detailed Directions by Car:
From South & West: Go via the A5 to Llangollen. At the traffic lights turn into Castle Street to the River bridge; From North & East: Take the A483 to A539 junction and then via Trefor to Llangollen River bridge. The Station is adjacent to the River Dee.

LOCOMOTION – THE NATIONAL RAILWAY MUSEUM AT SHILDON

Address: Locomotion, Shildon, County Durham DL14 1PQ	**Length of Line**: Over ½ mile
Telephone Nº: (01388) 777999	**Nº of Steam Locos**: 60 locomotives and other rail vehicles
Fax Nº: (01388) 771448	**Approx Nº of Visitors P.A.**: 60,000+
Year Formed: 2004	**Gauge**: Standard
Location: Shildon, County Durham	**Web site**: www.locomotion.uk.com

GENERAL INFORMATION

Nearest Mainline Station: Shildon (adjacent)
Nearest Bus Station: Durham
Car Parking: Available on site
Coach Parking: Available on site
Souvenir Shop(s): Yes
Food & Drinks: Yes

SPECIAL INFORMATION

This extensive site is the first regional branch of the National Railway Museum and houses vehicles from the National Collection in a purpose-built 6,000 square-foot building.

OPERATING INFORMATION

Opening Times: 2010 dates: Daily from 1st April to 4th October – 10.00am to 5.00pm. The Collection Building is open on Mondays and Tuesdays between 5th October 2010 to 31st March 2011 – 10.00am to 4.00pm. The rest of the site is open from Wednesday to Sunday during the Winter season – also from 10.00am to 4.00pm although the Museum is closed over the Christmas and New Year Holiday period.
Steam Working: During the Summer School Holidays and on special event days – please phone to confirm details.
Prices: Admission to the Museum is free of charge.
Train Rides: Adults £1.50   Concessions 75p

Detailed Directions by Car:
From All Parts: Exit the A1(M) at Junction 58 and take the A68 and the A6072 to Shildon. Follow the Brown tourist signs to Locomotion which is situated ¼ mile to the south-east of the Town Centre.

MANGAPPS RAILWAY MUSEUM

Address: Southminster Road, Burnham-on-Crouch, Essex CM0 8QQ
Telephone N°: (01621) 784898
Year Formed: 1989
Location of Line: Mangapps Farm
Length of Line: ¾ mile

N° of Steam Locos: 6
N° of Other Locos: 10
N° of Members: –
Annual Membership Fee: –
Approx N° of Visitors P.A.: 20,000
Gauge: Standard
Web site: www.mangapps.co.uk

GENERAL INFORMATION

Nearest Mainline Station: Burnham-on-Crouch (1 mile)
Nearest Bus Station: –
Car Parking: Ample free parking at site
Coach Parking: Ample free parking at site
Souvenir Shop(s): Yes
Food & Drinks: Yes – drinks and snacks only

SPECIAL INFORMATION

The Railway endeavours to recreate the atmosphere of an East Anglian light railway. It also includes an extensive museum with an emphasis on East Anglian items and signalling.

OPERATING INFORMATION

Opening Times: Closed during January and November, then open every weekend and Bank Holiday (except over Christmas). Open from 11.30am to 5.00pm. Santa Specials run during weekends in December. Please contact the railway for further details.
Steam Working: Bank Holiday Sundays and Mondays plus certain other dates. Please contact the railway for further details.
Prices: Adult – Steam £8.00;   Diesel £7.00
     Child – Steam £3.50;   Diesel £3.00
     Senior Citizen – Steam £7.00; Diesel £6.00
Note: Prices for special events may differ.

Detailed Directions by Car:
From South & West: From M25 take either the A12 or A127 and then the A130 to Rettendon Turnpike and then follow signs to Burnham; From North: From A12 take A414 to Oak Corner then follow signs to Burnham.

THE MIDDLETON RAILWAY

Address: The Station, Moor Road, Hunslet, Leeds LS10 2JQ **Telephone Nº**: (0113) 271-0320 **Year Formed**: 1960 **Location of Line**: Moor Road to Middleton Park **Length of Line**: 1½ miles	**Nº of Steam Locos**: 18 **Nº of Other Locos**: 10 **Annual Membership Fee**: Adults £15.00 **Approx Nº of Visitors P.A.**: 20,000 **Gauge**: Standard **Web Site**: www.middletonrailway.org.uk

GENERAL INFORMATION

Nearest Mainline Station: Leeds City (1 mile)
Nearest Bus Station: Leeds (1½ miles)
Car Parking: Free parking at site
Coach Parking: Free parking at site
Souvenir Shop(s): Yes
Food & Drinks: Yes

SPECIAL INFORMATION

Operating in every year since 1758, the railway still operates under its original Act of Parliament. Passenger services run from the station into Middleton Park. A large collection of preserved industrial steam and diesel engines are displayed, many of them more than 100 years old.

OPERATING INFORMATION

Opening Times: Weekends and Bank Holidays from Easter to the end of November plus Santa Specials in December. Also open on Wednesdays in August. Diesel services run at 40 minute intervals from 1.00pm to 4.20pm.
Steam Working: Every Sunday and Bank Holiday Monday from Easter to the end of November plus Santa Specials in December. Steam services run at 40 minute intervals from 11.00am to 4.20pm.
Prices: Adult £4.50
                   Child   £2.50
                   Family £12.00
                               (2 adults + 3 children)
Tickets provide for unlimited travel on the day of issue. Please send the railway a SAE for the timetable and details of special events or check the web site.
Note: Different prices may apply on Special Event days.

Detailed Directions by Car:
From the South: Take the M621 Northbound and exit at Junction 5. Turn right at the top of the slip road and take the 3rd exit at the roundabout. The Railway is 50 yards on the right; From the West: Take the M621 Southbound and exit at Junction 6. Turn left at the end of the slip road then left again into Moor Road at the next set of traffic lights. Bear right at the mini roundabout and the railway is on the left after 150 yards.

MID-HANTS RAILWAY (WATERCRESS LINE)

Address: The Railway Station, Alresford, Hampshire SO24 9JG
Telephone Nº: (01962) 733810 General enquiries; (01962) 734866 Timetable
Year Formed: 1977
Location of Line: Alresford to Alton
Length of Line: 10 miles

Nº of Steam Locos: 16
Nº of Other Locos: 8
Nº of Members: 3,500
Annual Membership Fee: Adult £20.00
Approx Nº of Visitors P.A.: 150,000
Gauge: Standard
Web Site: www.watercressline.co.uk

Photo courtesy of David Warwick

GENERAL INFORMATION

Nearest Mainline Station: Alton (adjacent) or Winchester (7 miles)
Nearest Bus Station: Winchester or Alton
Car Parking: Pay and display at Alton and Alresford Stations (Alresford free on Sundays & Bank Holidays)
Coach Parking: By arrangement at Alresford Station
Souvenir Shop(s): At Alresford, Ropley & Alton
Food & Drinks: Yes – Buffet on most trains. 'West Country' buffet at Alresford

SPECIAL INFORMATION

The railway runs through four fully restored stations and has a Loco yard and picnic area at Ropley.

OPERATING INFORMATION

Opening Times: Weekends and Bank Holidays from January to October plus Tuesday to Thursday from May to the end of July. Daily during the School holidays. Santa Specials run at weekends and on other dates in December.
Steam Working: All operating days although a Steam/DMU combination is sometimes in service.
Prices: Adult £12.00
Child (ages 2 to 16) £6.00
Family £30.00 (2 adults + 2 children)
A discount is available for pre-booked parties of 15 or more people. Write or call for a booking form.

Detailed Directions by Car:
From the East: Take the M25 then A3 and A31 to Alton; From the West: Exit the M3 at Junction 9 and take the A31 to Alresford Station.

MID-NORFOLK RAILWAY

Address: The Railway Station, Station Road, Dereham NR19 1DF	**N° of Steam Locos**: Visiting locos only
Telephone N°: (01362) 690633 or 851723	**N° of Other Locos**: 8
Year Formed: 1995	**N° of Members**: 1,000
Location: East Dereham to Wymondham	**Annual Membership Fee**: £16.00
Length of Line: 11 miles	**Approx N° of Visitors P.A.**: 16,000
	Gauge: Standard
	Web site: www.mnr.org.uk

GENERAL INFORMATION

Nearest Mainline Station: Wymondham (1 mile)
Nearest Bus Station: Wymondham or East Dereham – each ½ mile away
Car Parking: Available at Dereham Station
Coach Parking: Available at Dereham Station
Souvenir Shop(s): Yes – at Dereham Station
Food & Drinks: Yes – at Dereham Station

SPECIAL INFORMATION

The Mid-Norfolk Railway aims to preserve the former Great Eastern Railway from Wymondham to County School. The section from Wymondham to Dereham was opened to passenger and freight traffic in May 1999 and clearance work is now complete on the East Dereham to County School section.

OPERATING INFORMATION

Opening Times: 2010 dates: Every Sunday and Bank Holiday from 14th March to 24th October. Also open on Saturdays from 20th March to 23rd October, Wednesdays from 5th May to 27th October and Thursdays from 29th July to 26th August.
Steam Working: Weekends and Bank Holidays from 10th July to 30th August inclusive with a visiting Steam locomotive.
Prices: Adult Return £7.00 (Diesel)
Child Return £3.50 (Diesel)
Adult Return £10.00 (Steam days)
Child Return £5.00 (Steam days)

Detailed Directions by Car:
From All Parts: From the A47 bypass, turn into Dereham and follow the signs for the Town Centre. Turn right at the BP Garage – look out for the brown tourist signs – you will see the Station on your right.

MID-SUFFOLK LIGHT RAILWAY MUSEUM

Address: Brockford Station, Wetheringsett, Suffolk IP14 5PW **Telephone N°**: (01449) 766899 **Year Formed**: 1990 **Location of Line**: Wetheringsett, Suffolk **Length of Line**: ¼ mile	**N° of Steam Locos**: 2 (1 operational) **N° of Other Locos**: 1 **N° of Members**: 400 **Annual Membership Fee**: £12.00 **Approx N° of Visitors P.A.**: 2,000 **Gauge**: Standard **Web site**: www.mslr.org.uk

GENERAL INFORMATION

Nearest Mainline Station: Stowmarket
Nearest Bus Station: Ipswich
Car Parking: Available on site
Coach Parking: Available on site
Souvenir Shop(s): Yes
Food & Drinks: Yes

SPECIAL INFORMATION

The Mid-Suffolk Light Railway served the heart of the county for 50 years, despite being bankrupt before the first train ran. In a beautiful rural setting, the Museum seeks to preserve the memory of a unique branch line.

OPERATING INFORMATION

Opening Times: Sundays and Bank Holiday Mondays from Easter to the end of September and also on Wednesdays in August. Open from 11.00am to 5.00pm. Special events open at different times.
Steam Working: 2010 dates: 4th & 5th April; 2nd, 3rd, 30th & 31st May; 6th June; 4th July; 1st, 8th, 12th, 15th, 22nd, 29th & 30th August; 26th September. Possibly other dates – please contact the railway or check the web site for details.
Prices: Adult £5.00   Child £2.50
　　　　　Family Ticket £12.50
Tickets allow unlimited travel on the day of issue and act as season tickets for the calendar year (subject to conditions).

Detailed Directions by Car:
The Museum is situated 14 miles north of Ipswich and 28 miles south of Norwich, just off the A140. Look for Mendlesham TV mast and then follow the brown tourist signs from the A140.

MIDLAND RAILWAY – BUTTERLEY

Address: Butterley Station, Ripley, Derbyshire DE5 3QZ
Telephone Nº: (01773) 747674
Year Formed: 1969
Location of Line: Butterley, near Ripley
Length of Line: Standard gauge 3½ miles, Narrow gauge 0.8 mile

Nº of Steam Locos: 22 (+53 Other Locos)
Nº of Members: 2,000
Annual Membership Fee: £16.00
Approx Nº of Visitors P.A.: 130,000
Gauge: Standard, various Narrow gauges and miniature
Web: www.midlandrailwaycentre.co.uk

GENERAL INFORMATION

Nearest Mainline Station: Alfreton (6 miles)
Nearest Bus Station: Bus stop outside Butterley Station.
Car Parking: Free parking at site – ample space
Coach Parking: Free parking at site
Souvenir Shop(s): Yes – at Butterley and Swanwick
Food & Drinks: Yes – both sites + bar on train

SPECIAL INFORMATION

The Centre is a unique project with a huge Museum development together with narrow gauge, miniature & model railways as well as a country park and farm park. Includes an Award-winning Victorian Railwayman's church and Princess Royal Class Locomotive Trust Depot.

OPERATING INFORMATION

Opening Times: Open daily throughout the year (closed on Christmas Day and Boxing Day) – trains do not run every day it is open however.
Steam Working: Weekends and bank holidays throughout the year and most days in the school holidays. Phone for further details. 'Day Out With Thomas' 2010 events: 29th May to 2nd June; 4th to 8th August; 27th to 31st December.
Prices: Adult £10.95
Children £5.50
Senior Citizens £9.95
Family £29.70 (2 adults + 3 children)
Note: Some special events are more expensive.

Detailed Directions by Car:
From All Parts: From the M1 exit at Junction 28 and take the A38 towards Derby. The Centre is signposted at the junction with the B6179.

NATIONAL RAILWAY MUSEUM

Address: National Railway Museum, Leeman Road, York YO26 4XJ	**Nº of Steam Locos**: 79
Telephone Nº: 08448 153139	**Nº of Other Locos**: 37
Year Formed: 1975	**Approx Nº of Visitors P.A.**: 800,000
Location of Line: York	**Web site**: www.nrm.org.uk
Length of Line: Short demonstration line	

GENERAL INFORMATION

Nearest Mainline Station: York (¼ mile)
Nearest Bus Station: York (¼ mile)
Car Parking: On site long stay car park
Coach Parking: On site – free to pre-booked groups
Souvenir Shop(s): Yes
Food & Drinks: Yes

SPECIAL INFORMATION

The Museum is the largest of its kind in the world, housing the Nation's collection of locomotives, carriages, uniforms, posters and an extensive photographic archive. Special events and exhibitions run throughout the year. The Museum is the home of the Mallard – the fastest steam locomotive in the world and Shinkansen, the only Bullet train outside of Japan.

OPERATING INFORMATION

Opening Times: Open daily 10.00am to 6.00pm (closed on 24th, 25th and 26th of December)
Steam Working: School holidays – please phone to confirm details
Prices: Free admission for all
(Excludes some Special events and Steam rides)
Please phone 08448 153139 for further details.

Detailed Directions by Car:
The Museum is located in the centre of York, just behind the Railway Station. It is clearly signposted from all approaches to York.

NENE VALLEY RAILWAY

Address: Wansford Station, Stibbington, Peterborough PE8 6LR	**Nº of Steam Locos:** 17
Telephone Nº: (01780) 784444 enquiries; (01780) 784404 talking timetable	**Nº of Other Locos:** 11
	Nº of Members: 1,300
Year Formed: 1977	**Annual Membership Fee:** Adult £14.50; Child £8.50; Joint £22.00; OAP £8.50
Location: Off A1 to west of Peterborough	**Approx Nº of Visitors P.A.:** 65,000
Length of Line: 7½ miles	**Gauge:** Standard
	Web site: www.nvr.org.uk

GENERAL INFORMATION

Nearest Mainline Station: Peterborough (¾ mile)
Nearest Bus Station: Peterborough (Queensgate – ¾ mile)
Car Parking: Free parking at Wansford & Orton Mere
Coach Parking: Free coach parking at Wansford
Souvenir Shop(s): Yes
Food & Drinks: Yes

SPECIAL INFORMATION

The railway is truly international in flavour with British and Continental locomotives and rolling stock.

OPERATING INFORMATION

Opening Times: 2010 dates: Most weekends from March to 1st November. Also open mid-week on various dates from May to the end of August and also at various other times. Santa Specials run in December. Please contact the Railway for further details. Open 9.00am to 4.30pm.
Steam Working: Most services are steam hauled apart from on diesel days and times of high fire risk.
Prices: Adult £12.00 (Special events £14.00)
Child £6.00 (age 3-15) (Special events £7.00)
Family £30.00 (2 adult + 3 child) (Special £35.00)
Senior Citizens/Disabled £9.00 (Special £10.50)

Detailed Directions by Car:
The railway is situated off the southbound carriageway of the A1 between the A47 and A605 junctions – west of Peterborough and south of Stamford.

North Norfolk Railway

Address: Sheringham Station, Sheringham, Norfolk NR26 8RA
Telephone Nº: (01263) 820800
Year Formed: 1975
Location of Line: Sheringham to Holt via Weybourne
Length of Line: 5½ miles

Nº of Steam Locos: 5 (+ visiting locos)
Nº of Other Locos: 4
Nº of Members: 1,800 (M&GNRS)
Annual Membership Fee: £18.00 (Midland & Great Northern Railway Society)
Approx Nº of Visitors P.A.: 130,000
Gauge: Standard
Web site: www.nnrailway.co.uk

GENERAL INFORMATION

Nearest Mainline Station: Sheringham (200 yards)
Nearest Bus Station: Outside the Station
Car Parking: Adjacent to Sheringham and Holt
Coach Parking: Adjacent to Sheringham and Holt
Souvenir Shop(s): At Sheringham Station
Food & Drinks: Yes – main catering facilities at Sheringham Station. Light refreshments elsewhere.

SPECIAL INFORMATION

From 11th March 2010, Sheringham level crossing reconnects the North Norfolk Railway with the national network for an occasional use basis, rejoining two former sections of the Midland & Great Northern Joint Railway.

OPERATING INFORMATION

Opening Times: 2010 dates: Daily from 1st April to the 31st October plus weekends in March and Santa Specials in December. Special Events: Vintage Transport Day on 4th July; Beer Festival 16th to 18th July; Grand Steam Gala 3rd to 5th September.
Steam Working: 9.45am to 4.30pm (high season)
Prices: Adult £10.50
  Child £7.00   (Under 5's free of charge)
  Family £35.00 (2 adults + 2 children)
  Senior Citizens £9.50
The prices shown above are for all-day Rover tickets.

Detailed Directions by Car:
Sheringham Station is situated just off the A149. Holt Station is located at High Kelling, just off the A148.

NORTH TYNESIDE STEAM RAILWAY

Address: Stephenson Railway Museum, Middle Engine Lane, North Shields, NE29 8DX **Telephone Nº:** (0191) 200-7146 **Year Formed:** 1986 **Location:** Stephenson Railway Museum **Length of Line:** 1½ miles	**Nº of Steam Locos:** 5 **Nº of Other Locos:** 3 **Nº of Members:** 30 **Annual Membership Fee:** £9.00 **Approx Nº of Visitors P.A.:** 30,000 **Gauge:** Standard **Web site:** www.twmuseums.org.uk/stephenson

GENERAL INFORMATION

Nearest Mainline Station: Newcastle Central (5 miles)
Nearest Bus Station: North Shields
Car Parking: Free parking available on site
Coach Parking: Free parking available on site
Souvenir Shop(s): Yes
Food & Drinks: Hot drinks machine available

SPECIAL INFORMATION

A programme of events and activities is available from the Museum on request.

OPERATING INFORMATION

Opening Times: 2010 dates: Weekends and Bank Holidays from 3rd April and daily during School Holidays, 11.00am to 4.00pm.
Steam Working: Sundays and Bank Holiday Mondays from June to September.
Prices: Adult Return £2.10
Child Return £1.05
Family Return £5.25

Detailed Directions by Car:
The Railway is adjacent to the Silverlink Retail Park approximately ½ mile from the junction between the A19 and A1058. From the A19/A1058 junction look for the signs for 'Silverlink' before following the Brown tourist signs to the Stephenson Railway Museum.

NORTH YORKSHIRE MOORS RAILWAY

Address: Pickering Station, Pickering, North Yorkshire YO18 7AJ
Telephone Nº: (01751) 472508 (enquiries)
Year Formed: 1967
Location of Line: Pickering to Grosmont via stations at Levisham and Goathland
Length of Line: 18 miles
Nº of Steam Locos: 20

Nº of Other Locos: 12
Nº of Members: 8,000
Annual Membership Fee: Adult £18.00; Over 60's £14.00
Approx Nº of Visitors P.A.: 330,000
Gauge: Standard
Web site: www.nymr.co.uk

GENERAL INFORMATION

Nearest Mainline Station: Grosmont (adjacent to the NYMR station) or Whitby
Nearest Bus Station: Pickering (½ mile)
Car Parking: Available at each station
Coach Parking: Available at Pickering & Grosmont
Souvenir Shop(s): Yes – at Pickering, Goathland, and Grosmont Stations plus Grosmont MPD
Food & Drinks: Pickering, Grosmont & Goathland

SPECIAL INFORMATION

The NYMR runs through the spectacular North York Moors National Park and is the most popular steam railway in the country. As seen in 'Heartbeat' and the first Harry Potter film. The railway now operates extended services to and from Whitby.

OPERATING INFORMATION

Opening Times: 2010 dates: Open daily from 27th March to 31st October plus some other Winter dates and Santa Specials in December.
Steam Working: Usually daily – please phone the Railway for timetable information
Prices: Adult £16.00 (all-day travel)
Child £8.00 (all-day travel)
Family Tickets £33.00
(2 adults and up to 4 children)

Detailed Directions by Car:
From the South: Follow the A64 past York to the Malton bypass then take the A169 to Pickering; From the North: Take A171 towards Whitby then follow the minor road through Egton to Grosmont.

Northampton & Lamport Railway

Address: Pitsford & Bramford Station, Pitsford Road, Chapel Brampton, Northampton NN6 8BA **Telephone No:** (01604) 820327 (infoline) **Year Formed:** 1983 (became operational in November 1995) **Length of Line:** 1¼ miles at present	**No of Steam Locos:** 6 **No of Other Locos:** 10 **No of Members:** 600 **Annual Membership Fee:** £12.00 **Approx No of Visitors P.A.:** 20,000 **Gauge:** Standard **Web site:** www.nlr.org.uk

GENERAL INFORMATION

Nearest Mainline Station: Northampton (5 miles)
Nearest Bus Station: Northampton (5 miles)
Car Parking: Free parking at site
Coach Parking: Free parking at site
Souvenir Shop(s): Yes
Food & Drinks: Yes

SPECIAL INFORMATION

A developing railway – this became operational again on 18th November 1995.

OPERATING INFORMATION

Opening Times: Sundays and Bank holidays in April, May and October. Santa Specials in December. Also on various other detes throughout the year. Open 10.30am to 5.00pm though the last train runs at 3.45pm. Please contact the railway for a more detailed timetable.

Steam Working: Bank Holiday weekends, Santa Specials in December and various other dates. Please contact the railway for further information.

Prices: Adult £4.50
Child £3.50
Family £14.50 (2 adults + 2 children)
Senior Citizen £3.50

Fares may vary on Special Event days.

Detailed Directions by Car:
The station is situated along the Pitsford road at Chapel Brampton, approximately 5 miles north of Northampton. Heading north out of town, it is signposted to the right on the A5199 (A50) Welford Road at Chapel Brampton crossroads or on the left on the A508 Market Harborough road at the Pitsford turn.

NORTHANTS. IRONSTONE RAILWAY TRUST

Address: Hunsbury Hill Museum, Hunsbury Hill Country Park, West Hunsbury, Northampton NN4 9UW
Telephone Nº: (01604) 702031
Year Formed: 1974
Location of Line: Hunsbury Hill Country Park, Northampton
Length of Line: Two-thirds of a mile

Nº of Steam Locos: 3
Nº of Other Locos: 4
Nº of Members: Approximately 60
Annual Membership Fee: £10.00 Adult
Approx Nº of Visitors P.A.: Not known
Gauge: Standard
Web site: www.nirt.co.uk

GENERAL INFORMATION

Nearest Mainline Station: Northampton (2½ miles)
Nearest Bus Station: Northampton (3 miles)
Car Parking: Large free car park at the site
Coach Parking: Available at the site on request
Souvenir Shop(s): Yes
Food & Drinks: Yes

SPECIAL INFORMATION

The Railway has recently re-opened after a major rebuild and now operates along two-thirds of a mile of track. The Museum is dedicated to the Ironstone industry of Northamptonshire.

OPERATING INFORMATION

Opening Times: The museum is open during Easter weekend then on the first Sunday of the month from May to September and also on Bank Holidays throughout the year. Trains run at these times also. There may also be a number of special events throughout the year (including Santa Specials) – please contact the railway for further details.
Steam Working: An hourly service runs between 11.00am and 5.00pm.
Prices: Adult £3.00   Child £2.00
Concessions £1.50
Admission to the museum and site is free of charge but donations are always welcome.

Detailed Directions by Car:
Exit the M1 at Junction 15A, and follow the road for approximately ½ mile. Turn left onto the A43 and after approximately 1 mile take the 3rd exit at the roundabout onto Danes Camp Way (A45). After ½ mile take the 4th exit at the roundabout onto Hunsbury Hill Road. Continue over two mini-roundabouts past the Rose & Claret Public House. The entrance to Hunsbury Hill Country Park for the railway is on the left.

Paignton & Dartmouth Steam Railway

Address: Queen's Park Station, Torbay Road, Paignton TQ4 6AF
Telephone No: (01803) 555872
Year Formed: 1973
Location of Line: Paignton to Kingswear
Length of Line: 7 miles

No of Steam Locos: 6
No of Other Locos: 3
No of Members: –
Annual Membership Fee: –
Approx No of Visitors P.A.: 350,000
Gauge: Standard
Web site: www.dartmouthrailriver.co.uk

GENERAL INFORMATION

Nearest Mainline Station: Paignton (adjacent)
Nearest Bus Station: Paignton (2 minutes walk)
Car Parking: Multi-storey or Mainline Station
Coach Parking: Multi-storey (3 minutes walk)
Souvenir Shop(s): Yes – at Paignton & Kingswear
Food & Drinks: Yes – at Paignton & Kingswear

SPECIAL INFORMATION

A passenger ferry is available from Kingswear Station across to Dartmouth. Combined excursions are also available including train and river trips.

OPERATING INFORMATION

Opening Times: Open daily from May to September (inclusive). Also open on days in April, October and December. Please contact the railway for further information.
Steam Working: Trains run throughout the day from 10.30am to 5.00pm.
Prices: Adult Return £12.00 (Includes ferry charge)
Child Return £8.50 (Includes ferry charge)
Family Return £35.00
 2 adults and 2 children
 (Includes ferry charge)
Note: Cheaper fares are charged for shorter journeys

Detailed Directions by Car:
From All Parts: Take the M5 to Exeter and then the A380 to Paignton.

PEAK RAIL PLC

Address: Matlock Station, Matlock, Derbyshire DE4 3NA
Telephone Nº: (01629) 580381
Fax Nº: (01629) 760645
Year Formed: 1975
Location of Line: Matlock Riverside to Rowsley South

Length of Line: Approximately 4 miles
Nº of Steam Locos: 5 **Other Locos:** 20+
Nº of Members: 1,700
Annual Adult Membership Fee: £16.00
Approx Nº of Visitors P.A.: 60,000
Gauge: Standard
Web site: www.peakrail.co.uk

GENERAL INFO

Nearest Mainline Station: Matlock (500 yards)
Nearest Bus Station: Matlock
Car Parking: Paid car parking at Matlock Station. 200 free parking spaces available at Rowsley South Station and 20 free spaces at Darley Dale Station
Coach Parking: Free parking at Rowsley South
Souvenir Shop(s): Yes
Food & Drinks: Yes

SPECIAL INFO

The Palatine Restaurant Car is available whilst travelling on the train and caters for Sunday Lunches, Teas and Party Bookings. Coach parties are welcomed when the railway is operating.

OPERATING INFO

Opening Times: Sundays in January, February and November. Weekends during the rest of the year. Also Wednesdays in May, June and July, Tuesdays and Wednesdays in August and the first two weeks of September.
Steam Working: All services throughout the year.
Prices: Adult Return £6.50
Children – Under-3's Free
Children – Ages 3-5 £1.50
Children – Ages 6-15 £3.50
Senior Citizen Return £5.10
Family Ticket £19.50
(2 adults + 3 children)

Detailed Directions by Car:
Exit the M1 at Junctions 28, 29 or 30 and follow signs towards Matlock. From North and South take A6 direct to Matlock. From Stoke-on-Trent, take the A52 to Ashbourne, then the A5035 to Matlock. Upon reaching Matlock follow the brown tourist signs.

PLYM VALLEY RAILWAY

Address: Marsh Mills Station, Coypool Road, Plympton, Plymouth PL7 4NW **Telephone Nº:** (01752) 330881 **Year Formed:** 1980 **Location of Line:** Marsh Mills to Lee Moor Crossing, Plympton **Length of Line:** ¾ mile	**Nº of Steam Locos:** 2 **Nº of Other Locos:** 4 **Nº of Members:** 200 **Annual Membership Fee:** £10.00 **Approx Nº of Visitors P.A.:** 5,000 **Gauge:** Standard **Web site:** www.plymrail.co.uk

GENERAL INFORMATION

Nearest Mainline Station: Plymouth (4 miles)
Nearest Bus Station: Plymouth (3 miles)
Car Parking: Available on site
Coach Parking: Available on site
Souvenir Shop(s): Yes
Food & Drinks: Light snacks available

SPECIAL INFORMATION

The ultimate aim of the railway is to rebuild a 1¼ mile section of the ex-Great Western branch line which ran from Tavistock Junction, just outside of Plymouth, through to Launceston. The section to be rebuilt runs from Marsh Mills to Plym Bridge.

OPERATING INFORMATION

Opening Times: Open for static viewing on most Sundays from 11.00am to 5.00pm. Please check the railway's web site or contact the railway directly for information about operating days. Trains run between 1.00pm to 4.00pm on these dates.
Steam Working: Most operating days. Please contact the railway for further details.
Prices: Adult Return £3.00
Child Return £1.50
Note: There is no charge to visit the station.

Detailed Directions by Car:
Leave the A38 at the Marsh Mills turn-off and take the B3416 towards Plympton. Turn left into Coypool Road just after the McDonalds restaurant. From Plymouth City Centre, take the A374 to Marsh Mills, then as above.

PONTYPOOL & BLAENAVON RAILWAY

Address: 13a Broad Street, Blaenavon, Torfaen   NP4 9ND
e-mail: info@pbrly.co.uk
Telephone Nº: (01495) 792263
Year Formed: 1980 (Opened 1983)
Location of Line: Just off the B4248 between Blaenavon and Brynmawr
Length of Line: ¾ mile

Nº of Steam Locos: 9
Nº of Other Locos: 7 + 3 DMUs
Nº of Members: 200
Annual Membership Fee: £12.00
Approx Nº of Visitors P.A.: 5,700
Gauge: Standard
Web site: www.pontypool-and-blaenavon.co.uk

GENERAL INFORMATION

Nearest Mainline Station: Abergavenny (5 miles)
Nearest Bus Station: Blaenavon Town (1½ miles) – regular bus service within ¼ mile (except Sundays)
Car Parking: Free parking for 50 cars on site
Coach Parking: Available on site
Souvenir Shop(s): Yes – at the Station and also a shop at 13 Broad Street, Blaenavon
Food & Drinks: Light refreshments on the train and at the station.

SPECIAL INFORMATION

The railway operates over very steep gradients, is run entirely by volunteers and is the highest standard gauge preserved railway in England and Wales.

OPERATING INFORMATION

Opening Times: 2010 dates: Every weekend and Bank Holiday Monday 5th June to 10th October. Santa Specials and other Special events also run. Please phone the Railway for details or check the web site.
Steam Working: Trains are steam-hauled during Peak days and special steam days. Diesel locos or DMUs may be used on quiet days. Please contact the Railway for further information.
Prices: Adult £4.50
Child £2.25
Family £12.00 (2 adults + 3 children)
Fares and conditions may vary for Special Events.

Detailed Directions by Car:
From All Parts: The railway is situated just off the B4248 between Blaenavon and Brynmawr and is well signposted as you approach Blaenavon. Use Junction 25A if using the M4 from the East, or Junction 26 from the West. Head for Pontypool. From the Midlands use the M50, A40 then A465 to Brynmawr. From North & West Wales consider using the 'Heads of the Valleys' A465 to Brynmawr. As you approach the Railway, look out for the Colliery water tower – you can't miss it!

RAILWAY PRESERVATION SOCIETY OF IRELAND

Address: Castleview, Whitehead,
Co. Antrim, Northern Ireland BT38 9NA
Telephone Nº: (028) 2826-0803
Year Formed: 1964
Location of Line: Whitehead, Co. Antrim
Length of Line: ¼ mile
Gauge: Irish Standard

Nº of Steam Locos: 9
Nº of Other Locos: 5
Nº of Members: 1,100
Annual Membership Fee: Adult £25.00;
Senior £20.00; Junior £15.00; Family £60.00
Approx Nº of Visitors P.A.: 10,000
Web Site: www.rpsi-online.org

GENERAL INFORMATION

Nearest NIR Station: Whitehead (½ mile)
Nearest Bus Station: Whitehead (½ mile)
Car Parking: Free parking at site
Coach Parking: Free parking at site
Souvenir Shop(s): Yes
Food & Drinks: Yes

SPECIAL INFORMATION

The Society is the only Main Line Steam Operator in
Ireland.

OPERATING INFORMATION

Opening Times: Sundays in the Summer and also
during Easter and Christmas. There is also a regular
timetable of main line excursions. Please check the
web site or phone for further details.
Steam Working: 2.00pm to 5.00pm at Whitehead
Prices: Depends on the event or the destination of
main line excursions

Detailed Directions by Car:
Whitehead is situated about 15 miles to the North of Belfast just off the A2 between Larne and Carrickfergus. The
location is clearly signposted in Whitehead.

RIBBLE STEAM RAILWAY

Address: Chain Caul Road, Preston, PR2 2PD
Telephone Nº: (01772) 728800
Year Formed: 2005
Location: West of Preston City Centre
Length of Line: 3 mile round trip

Nº of Steam Locos: 23
Nº of Other Locos: 19
Nº of Members: 400
Annual Membership Fee: £12.00
Approx Nº of Visitors P.A.: 20,000+
Gauge: Standard
Web site: www.ribblesteam.org.uk

GENERAL INFORMATION

Nearest Mainline Station: Preston (2 miles)
Nearest Bus Station: Preston (2 miles)
Car Parking: Available on site
Coach Parking: Available on site
Souvenir Shop(s): Yes
Food & Drinks: Available

SPECIAL INFORMATION

The line traverses a swing bridge across the Marina entrance – the only preserved steam line in Britain to have such a feature! The railway was originally set up in the old LYR Steam shed at Southport in 1976 but moved to the current location in 2005.

OPERATING INFORMATION

Opening Times: 2010 dates: Open 10.30am to 5.00pm on weekends and Bank Holidays from April to 3rd October. Also open on Wednesdays in August and Santa specials on weekends in December. Please contact the railway for further details.
Steam Working: On all days when the railway is open to the public. Trains run hourly from 11.00am to 4.00pm.
Prices: Adult Return £5.50
         Child Return £3.50
         Family Return £15.00
Note: Different prices may apply for Special Events.

Detailed Directions by Car:
From All Parts: The Railway is located on the Riversway/Docklands Business and Residential Park, just off the A583 Lytham/Blackpool road and approximately 1½ miles to the west of Preston City Centre. Follow the Brown Tourist signs from the A583 for the railway.

ROYAL DEESIDE RAILWAY

Address: Milton of Crathes, Crathes, Banchory AB31 5QH **Telephone Nº**: (01330) 844416 **Year Formed**: 1996 **Location of Line**: Milton of Crathes **Length of Line**: 1 mile	**Nº of Steam Locos**: 1 **Nº of Other Locos**: 2 **Nº of Members**: 250 **Annual Membership Fee**: £15.00 **Approx Nº of Visitors P.A.**: 3,000 **Gauge**: Standard **Web site**: www.deeside-railway.co.uk

GENERAL INFORMATION

Nearest Mainline Station: Aberdeen (14 miles)
Nearest Bus Station: Stagecoach Bluebird bus stop nearby on A93.
Car Parking: Free parking available on site
Coach Parking: Free parking available on site
Souvenir Shop(s): Yes – inside a static carriage
Food & Drinks: Yes – inside a static carriage

SPECIAL INFORMATION

The railway is pleased to have the Andrew Barclay saddle tank "Bon Accord" available for steam operation on some dates in 2010.

OPERATING INFORMATION

Opening Times: 2010 dates: A Café with light refreshments, shop and display is located in a static carriage and opens Saturday and Sunday afternoons 12.00pm to 5.00pm from 11th April to 26th September. Brake van trips run from 12.00pm to 4.30pm on Sunday afternoons during this period and also for Santa Specials each weekend from 28th November to 19th December.
Steam Working: Last weekend in the month from May to August.
Prices: Adults £3.00 (£5.00 Steam days)
Children £1.50 (£2.50 Steam days)
Senior Citizens £2.00 (£3.00 Steam days)

Detailed Directions by Car:
From the South: Take the A90 to Stonehaven. Exit onto the B979 for Stonehaven and follow into the town square. Turn left at the traffic lights and follow signs for the A957 to Banchory (Historic Slug Road). Follow this road for 14 mile via Durris to Crathes and the junction with the A93. Turn left and follow the Brown Tourist signs, turning left for the railway after approximately 600 yards; From the North & West: Follow the A980 to Banchory and turn left onto the A93. Turn right following the Brown Tourist signs for the railway.

RUSHDEN TRANSPORT MUSEUM

Address: Rushden Station, Station Approach, Rushden, NN10 0AW	**Nº of Steam Locos**: 3
	Nº of Other Locos: 3
Telephone Nº: (01933) 318988	**Nº of Members**: Approximately 600
Year Formed: 1985	**Annual Membership Fee**: –
Location of Line: Rushden, Northants.	**Approx Nº of Visitors P.A.**: 5,000
Length of Line: ¼ mile	**Gauge**: Standard
	Web site: www.rhts.co.uk

GENERAL INFORMATION

Nearest Mainline Station: Wellingborough (5 miles)
Nearest Bus Station: Northampton (14 miles)
Car Parking: Available on site. On operating days a nearby public car park must be used.
Coach Parking: None
Souvenir Shop(s): Yes
Food & Drinks: Available on operating weekends

SPECIAL INFORMATION

The Rushden Transport Museum is situated in the old Midland Railway Station of 1894 which once formed part of the Wellingborough to Higham Ferrers branch line. Taken over by the Rushden Historical Transport Society in 1984 the station also provides the society with a social club.

OPERATING INFORMATION

Opening Times: Sundays from Easter until the end of October, open from 10.00am to 4.00pm. Trains operate on one weekend a month. Please contact the Museum or check the web site for further details.
Steam Working: Please contact the Museum for further details.
Prices: Adults £3.00
Children £1.50
Concessions £1.50
Note: Higher prices may be charged during special event days.

Detailed Directions by Car:
From All Parts: Take the A6 to the Rushden Bypass (to the south of the A45) and turn into John Clark Way by the large grey warehouses. The Station is located on the right-hand side of the road after approximately 400 yards.

RUTLAND RAILWAY MUSEUM

Address: Cottesmore Iron Ore Mines Siding, Ashwell Road, Cottesmore, Oakham, Rutland LE15 7BX **Telephone Nº**: (01572) 813203 **Year Formed**: 1979 **Location of Line**: Between the villages of Cottesmore and Ashwell **Length of Line**: ¾ mile	**Nº of Steam Locos**: 13 **Nº of Other Locos**: 13 **Nº of Members**: 275 **Annual Membership Fee**: £10.00 **Approx Nº of Visitors P.A.**: 8,000 **Gauge**: Standard **Web site**: www.rutlandrailwaymuseum.org.uk

GENERAL INFORMATION

Nearest Mainline Station: Oakham (4 miles)
Nearest Bus Station: Cottesmore/Ashwell (1½ miles)
Car Parking: Available at the site
Coach Parking: Limited space available
Souvenir Shop(s): On open days
Food & Drinks: On open days

SPECIAL INFORMATION

This Industrial Railway Heritage centre is located at the end of the former Ashwell-Cottesmore mineral branch and is based at the former exchange sidings.

OPERATING INFORMATION

Opening Times: Static viewing on Sundays from 11.00am to 4.00pm plus Tuesday and Thursday afternoons throughout the year.
Steam Working: 2010 dates: Santa Specials run on on 19th & 20th December. Please contact the railway for further details and dates for other events. Pre-booked Driver experience days are available.
Prices: Adult £4.00
　　　　　Child £2.00 (no charge for under 5's)
Prices shown are for admission to the site on steam operating days. Train rides are an additional fee. Special prices apply to Santa Specials in December.

Detailed Directions by Car:
From All Parts: The Museum is situated 4 miles north of Oakham between Ashwell and Cottesmore. Follow the brown tourist signs from the B668 Oakham to A1 road or the signs from the A606 Stamford to Oakham Road.

SCOTTISH INDUSTRIAL RAILWAY CENTRE

Address: Dunaskin Open Air Museum, Waterside, Patna, Ayrshire KA6 7JF
Telephone Nº: (01292) 313579 (Evenings & Weekends)
Year Formed: 1974
Location of Line: Dunaskin Ironworks
Length of Line: A third of a mile

Nº of Steam Locos: 9
Nº of Other Locos: 15
Nº of Members: 180
Annual Membership Fee: £12.50
Approx Nº of Visitors P.A.: 3,500
Gauge: Standard
Web site: www.arpg.org.uk

GENERAL INFORMATION

Nearest Mainline Station: Ayr (10 miles)
Nearest Bus Station: ½ hourly bus service from Ayr – phone (01292) 613500 for more information
Car Parking: Free parking available at the site
Coach Parking: Free parking available at the site
Souvenir Shop(s): Yes
Food & Drinks: Soft drinks and confectionery only

SPECIAL INFORMATION

The Railway is located at the former Dunaskin Heritage Centre which was unfortunately forced to close in 2006.

OPERATING INFORMATION

Opening Times: 2010 dates: 30th May; 27th June; 5th and 6th September. Also open on every Sunday during July and August. Open 11.00am to 4.30pm on all the above dates.
Steam Working: On all the above dates subject to locomotive availability. If a steam locomotive is not available for use on these date, Brake van rides will be offered as an alternative. Please contact the railway or check the web site for further details.
Prices: Adult £3.00
Child £2.00
Family Tickets £8.00

Detailed Directions by Car:
From All Parts: Dunaskin Open Air Museum is located adjacent to the A713 Ayr to Castle Douglas road approximately 10 miles to the southwest of Ayr.

SEVERN VALLEY RAILWAY

Address: Railway Station, Bewdley, Worcestershire   DY12 1BG
Telephone Nº: (01299) 403816
Year Formed: 1965
Location of Line: Kidderminster (Worcs.) to Bridgnorth (Shropshire)
Length of Line: 16 miles

Nº of Steam Locos: 27
Nº of Other Locos: 12
Nº of Members: 13,000
Annual Membership Fee: Adult £17.00
Approx Nº of Passengers P.A.: 248,000
Gauge: Standard
Web site: www.svr.co.uk

GENERAL INFORMATION

Nearest Mainline Station: Kidderminster (adjacent)
Nearest Bus Station: Kidderminster (500 yards)
Car Parking: Large car park at Kidderminster. Spaces also available at other stations.
Coach Parking: At Kidderminster
Souvenir Shop(s): At Kidderminster & Bridgnorth
Food & Drinks: On most trains. Also at Bewdley, Bridgnorth, Kidderminster and The Engine House

SPECIAL INFORMATION

The SVR has numerous special events including an Autumn Steam Gala, 1940's weekend, Classic Car & Bike Day and visits by Santa! 'The Engine House', the railway's visitor and education centre, is a further attraction at Highley.

OPERATING INFORMATION

Opening Times: 2010 dates: Weekends throughout the year. Also daily from 1st May to 3rd October and during local School Holidays.
Steam Working: Train times vary depending on timetable information. Phone for details.
Prices: Adult Day Rover £15.50
              Child Day Rover £8.00
              Senior Citizen Day Rover £13.50
              Family Day Rover £42.00
                      (2 adults + 4 children)
Note: Entrance to The Engine House is now included in the above prices.

Detailed Directions by Car:
For Kidderminster take M5 and exit Junction 3 or Junction 6. Follow the brown tourist signs for the railway; From the South: Take the M40 then M42 to Junction 1 for the A448 from Bromsgrove to Kidderminster.

SNIBSTON COLLIERY RAILWAY

Address: Ashby Road, Coalville, LE67 3LN **Telephone N°**: (01530) 278444 **Year Formed**: 2001 **Location of Line**: Snibston Colliery **Length of Line**: 1,100 yards	**N° of Steam Locos**: 4 **N° of Other Locos**: 2 **N° of Members**: – **Approx N° of Visitors P.A.**: 100,000 **Gauge**: Standard **Web site**: www.snibston.com

GENERAL INFORMATION

Nearest Mainline Station: Loughborough (10 miles)
Nearest Bus Station: Loughborough (10 miles)
Car Parking: Available on site
Coach Parking: Available on site
Souvenir Shop(s): Yes
Food & Drinks: Available

SPECIAL INFORMATION

The Railway is located on the site of the former Snibston Colliery which also hosts an interactive museum, outside play areas, a Country Park and a nature reserve.

OPERATING INFORMATION

Opening Times: The museum is open daily except for Christmas Day, Boxing Day and a two week break in January. Open from 10.00am to 3.00pm or 4.00pm, depending on the time of the year. Trains operate only on certain dates. Please contact the Museum for further information.

Steam Working: No usual steam operation. Please contact the Museum for details.

Prices: Adults £6.75 (Train rides £1.25 extra)
Children £4.50 (Trains rides 75p extra)
Concessions £4.75 (Train rides £1.25 extra)
Family £20.00 (2+2) or £22.00 (2 + 3) (Train rides £3.20 extra)

Detailed Directions by Car:
From All Parts: Exit the A42 at the A511 (Coalville) exit and follow the signs for Snibston.

Somerset & Dorset Railway Trust Museum

Address: The Railway Station, Washford, Somerset TA23 0PP	**Nº of Steam Locos**: 2
Telephone Nº: (01984) 640869	**Nº of Other Locos**: 1
Year Formed: 1966	**Nº of Members**: –
Location of Line: Washford Station	**Annual Membership Fee**: £18.00 (Adult)
Length of Line: Station sidings only	**Approx Nº of Visitors P.A.**: 3,000
	Gauge: Standard
	Web site: www.sdrt.org.uk

GENERAL INFORMATION

Nearest Mainline Station: Taunton (17 miles)
Nearest Bus Station: Taunton (17 miles)
Car Parking: Available on site
Coach Parking: None
Souvenir Shop(s): Yes
Food & Drinks: None

SPECIAL INFORMATION

The Museum of the Somerset & Dorset Railway Trust contains a mass of exhibits about and memorabilia of this much loved line. This includes a reconstruction of Midford signal box and carriages and wagons including some undergoing restoration.

OPERATING INFORMATION

Opening Times: 2010 dates: 20th, 21st and 25th to 28th March; 2nd to 15th April; daily from 1st May to 3rd October. Also open on 28th and 29th December for a Winter Steam Festival. Open from 10.30am to 5.00pm on these dates. Please check the Museum's web site for further details.
Steam Working: Please contact the Museum or check the web site for further details.
Prices: Adult £2.00
    Child £1.00
    Family £5.00

Detailed Directions by Car:
The Museum is located at the Railway Station in Washford Village on the A39 Bridgwater to Minehead road.

SOUTH DEVON RAILWAY

Address: Buckfastleigh Station, Buckfastleigh, Devon TQ11 0DZ	**N° of Steam Locos**: 16
Telephone N°: (0845) 345-1427	**N° of Other Locos**: 7
Year Formed: 1969	**N° of Members**: 2,000
Location of Line: Totnes to Buckfastleigh via Staverton	**Annual Membership Fee**: £15.00
	Approx N° of Visitors P.A.: 100,000
	Gauge: Standard
Length of Line: 7 miles	**Web Site**: www.southdevonrailway.co.uk

GENERAL INFORMATION

Nearest Mainline Station: Totnes (¼ mile)
Nearest Bus Station: Totnes (½ mile), Buckfastleigh (Station Road)
Car Parking: Free parking at Buckfastleigh, Council/BR parking at Totnes
Coach Parking: As above
Souvenir Shop(s): Yes – at Buckfastleigh
Food & Drinks: Yes – at Buckfastleigh & on train

SPECIAL INFORMATION

The railway was opened in 1872 as the Totnes, Buckfastleigh & Ashburton Railway.

OPERATING INFORMATION

Opening Times: 2010 dates: Daily from 20th March to 31st October. Santa Specials also run in December. Please contact the railway for further details.
Steam Working: Almost all trains are steam hauled.
Prices: Adult Return £10.00
             Child Return £6.00
             Family Return £29.80
                   (2 adults + 2 children)
             Senior Citizen Return £9.50
Note: Extra discounts are available for large groups.

Detailed Directions by Car:
Buckfastleigh is half way between Exeter and Plymouth on the A38 Devon Expressway. Totnes can be reached by taking the A385 from Paignton and Torquay. Brown tourist signs give directions for the railway.

SPA VALLEY RAILWAY

Address: West Station, Tunbridge Wells, Kent TN2 5QY	**N° of Steam Locos:** 10
Telephone N°: (01892) 537715	**N° of Other Locos:** 9
Year Formed: 1985	**N° of Members:** Approximately 660
Location of Line: Tunbridge Wells West to Groombridge	**Annual Membership Fee:** £15.00
	Approx N° of Visitors P.A.: 30,000
Length: 5 miles	**Gauge:** Standard
	Web Site: www.spavalleyrailway.co.uk

Photo courtesy of David Staines

GENERAL INFORMATION

Nearest Mainline Station: Tunbridge Wells Central (½ mile) or Eridge (once the line extension is open)
Nearest Bus Stop: Outside Sainsbury's (100yds)
Car Parking: Available nearby
Coach Parking: Coach station in Montacute Road (150 yards)
Souvenir Shop(s): Yes
Food & Drinks: Yes

SPECIAL INFORMATION

The Railway's Tunbridge Wells Terminus is in a historic and unique L.B. & S.C.R. engine shed. An extension of the line to Groombridge is now open and tickets inclusive of entry to Groombridge Place Manor House and Gardens are available.

OPERATING INFORMATION

Opening Times: 2010 dates: Weekends from 2nd April to 31st October. Some weekdays during School Holidays and also Santa Specials during December. Please contact the railway for further details.
Steam Working: Most services are steam-hauled. Trains run from 10.30am to 5.00pm (11.00am to 3.30pm midweek and during low season).
Prices: Adult Return £9.00
  Child Return £4.50
  Senior Citizen Return £8.00
  Family Return £23.00 (2 adult + 2 child)
Discounts are available for groups of 20 or more.
Fares vary on some special event days.
Fares allow unlimited travel on the day of issue except for special event days.

Detailed Directions by Car:
The Spa Valley Railway is in the southern part of Tunbridge Wells, 100 yards off the A26. Station is adjacent to Sainsbury's and Homebase. Car Parks are nearby in Major Yorks Road, Union House & Linden Close.

STEAM – MUSEUM OF THE GREAT WESTERN RAILWAY

Address: STEAM – Museum of the Great Western Railway, Kemble Drive, Swindon SN2 2TA
Telephone Nº: (01793) 466646
Year Formed: 2000

Nº of Steam Locos: 6
Nº of Other Locos: 1
Approx Nº of Visitors P.A.: 100,000
Web site: www.swindon.gov.uk/steam

GENERAL INFORMATION

Nearest Mainline Station: Swindon (10 min. walk)
Nearest Bus Station: Swindon (10 minute walk)
Car Parking: Ample parking space available in the Outlet Centre (charges apply)
Coach Parking: Free parking on site and nearby
Souvenir Shop(s): Yes
Food & Drinks: Yes

SPECIAL INFORMATION

STEAM tells the story of the men and women who built the Great Western Railway.

OPERATING INFORMATION

Opening Times: Open daily all year round from 10.00am to 5.00pm. Closed on 25th, 26th December and 1st January.
Steam Working: During some special events only – please contact the Museum for details.
Prices: Adult Tickets £6.40
Child Tickets £4.25
Family Tickets £17.00
Senior Citizen Tickets £4.25
Children under 3 are admitted free
Note: Season tickets are also available

Detailed Directions by Car:
Exit the M4 at Junction 16 and follow the brown tourist signs to 'Outlet Centre'. Similarly follow the brown signs from all other major routes.   From the Railway Station: STEAM is a short walk and is accessible through the pedestrian tunnel – entrance by Emlyn Square.

STRATHSPEY STEAM RAILWAY

Address: Aviemore Station, Dalfaber Road, Aviemore, Inverness-shire, PH22 1PY
Telephone Nº: (01479) 810725
Year Formed: 1971
Location of Line: Aviemore to Boat of Garten and Broomhill, Inverness-shire
Length of Line: 9½ miles at present

Nº of Steam Locos: 7
Nº of Other Locos: 10
Nº of Members: 850
Annual Membership Fee: £21.00
Approx Nº of Visitors P.A.: 56,000
Gauge: Standard
Web site: www.strathspeyrailway.co.uk

GENERAL INFORMATION

Nearest Mainline Station: Aviemore – Strathspey trains depart from Platform 3
Nearest Bus Station: Aviemore (adjacent)
Car Parking: Available at all stations
Coach Parking: Available at Aviemore and Broomhill stations
Souvenir Shop(s): Yes – at Aviemore and Boat of Garten Stations
Food & Drinks: Available on Steam trains only

SPECIAL INFORMATION

The railway featured in the BBC series 'Monarch of the Glen' and operates from Aviemore Station.

OPERATING INFORMATION

Opening Times: Daily in July and August, most days in April, May, June, September and October and other dates in December. Phone for details. Generally open from 9.30am to 4.30pm.
Steam Working: Most trains are steam-hauled but diesel power is used whenever necessary. Please phone the Railway for details.
Prices: Adult Return £10.50
　　　　　　　Child Return £5.25
　　　　　　　Family Return £26.00
　　　　　　　(2 adults + up to 3 children)
Day Rover tickets are available for £18.00

Detailed Directions by Car:
For Aviemore Station from South: Take the A9 then B970 and turn left between the railway & river bridges. For Boat of Garten from North; Take the A9 then A938 to Carr Bridge, then B9153 and A95 and follow the signs; From North East: Take A95 to Boat of Garten or Broomhill (3½ miles South from Grantown-on-Spey.

SWANAGE RAILWAY

Address: Station House, Railway Station, Swanage, Dorset BH19 1HB **Telephone N°**: (01929) 425800 **Year Formed**: 1976 **Location of Line**: Swanage to Norden **Length of Line**: 6 miles **Gauge**: Standard	**N° of Steam Locos**: 5 **N° of Other Locos**: 4 **N° of Members**: 4,200 **Annual Membership Fee**: Adult £18.00; Junior/Senior Citizen £12.00; Family 36.00 **Approx N° of Visitors P.A.**: 201,448 (exact figures for 2007) **Web site**: www.swanagerailway.co.uk

GENERAL INFORMATION

Nearest Mainline Station: Wareham (10 miles)
Nearest Bus Station: Swanage Station (adjacent)
Car Parking: Park & Ride at Norden. Public car parks in Swanage (5 minutes walk)
Coach Parking: Available at Norden
Souvenir Shop(s): Yes – at Swanage Station
Food & Drinks: Yes – buffet available on trains and also Swanage Station Buffet and at Norden.

SPECIAL INFORMATION

The railway runs along part of the route of the old Swanage to Wareham railway, opened in 1885.

OPERATING INFORMATION

Opening Times: Weekends from mid-February and daily from Easter to October. Also open on some other dates throughout the year. Open from 9.30am to 5.00pm.
Steam Working: Most services are steam-hauled. Please check with the Railway for further details.
Prices: Adult Return £9.00
Child Return £7.00
Family Ticket £26.00

Detailed Directions by Car:
Norden Park & Ride Station is situated off the A351 on the approach to Corfe Castle. Swanage Station is situated in the centre of the town, just a few minutes walk from the beach. Take the A351 to reach Swanage.

Swindon & Cricklade Railway

Address: Blunsdon Station, Tadpole Lane, Blunsdon, Swindon, Wilts SN25 2DA **Phone Nº:** (01793) 771615 **Year Formed:** 1978 **Location of Line:** Blunsdon to Hayes Knoll **Length of Line:** 1½ miles	**Nº of Steam Locos:** 6 **Nº of Other Locos:** 7 **Nº of Members:** 700 **Annual Membership Fee:** £14.00 **Approx Nº of Visitors P.A.:** 16,000 **Gauge:** Standard

GENERAL INFORMATION

Nearest Mainline Station: Swindon (5 miles)
Nearest Bus Station: Bus stop at Oakhurst (¾ mile)
Car Parking: Free parking at Blunsdon Station
Coach Parking: Free parking at Blunsdon Station
Souvenir Shop(s): Yes
Food & Drinks: Yes

SPECIAL INFORMATION

The Engine Shed at Hayes Knoll Station is open to the public.

Web site: www.swindon-cricklade-railway.org

OPERATING INFORMATION

Opening Times: The Railway is open every weekend and Bank Holiday throughout the year. Santa Specials run in December and other various special events throughout the year also have Steam train rides. Open 11.00am to 4.00pm.
Steam Working: Every Sunday from Easter until the end of October and certain other dates – please contact the railway for further details.
Prices: Adult £6.00   Child £4.00
                  Concessions £5.00
                  Family £18.00
Prices are different for special events.

Detailed Directions by Car:
From the M4: Exit the M4 at Junction 15 and follow the A419. Turn left at Blunsdon Stadium and follow the signs for the Railway: From Cirencester: Follow the A419 to the traffic lights at the top of Blunsdon Hill, then turn right and follow signs for the railway.

TANFIELD RAILWAY

Address: Marley Hill Engine Shed,
Old Marley Hill, Gateshead, Tyne & Wear
NE16 5ET
Telephone Nº: 0845 463-4938
Year Formed: 1976
Location of Line: Between Sunniside &
East Tanfield, Co. Durham
Length of Line: 3 miles

Nº of Steam Locos: 29 Standard, 2 Narrow
Nº Other Locos: 12 Standard, 15 Narrow
Nº of Members: 150
Annual Membership Fee: £9.00 (Adult)
Approx Nº of Visitors P.A.: 40,000
Gauge: Standard and Narrow gauge
Web site: www.tanfield-railway.co.uk

GENERAL INFORMATION

Nearest Mainline Station: Newcastle-upon-Tyne
(8 miles)
Nearest Bus St'n: Gateshead Interchange (6 miles)
Car Parking: Spaces for 150 cars at Andrews House
and 100 spaces at East Tanfield
Coach Parking: Spaces for 6 or 7 coaches only
Souvenir Shop(s): Yes
Food & Drinks: Yes – light snacks only

SPECIAL INFORMATION

Tanfield Railway is the oldest existing railway in use
– it was originally opened in 1725. It also runs
beside The Causey Arch, the oldest railway bridge in
the world.

OPERATING INFORMATION

Opening Times: Every Sunday & Bank Holiday
Monday throughout the year. Also opens on
Wednesdays & Thursdays in Summer school
holidays. Santa Specials run in December.
Steam Working: Most trains are steam-hauled and
run from 11.00am to 4.00pm (11.30am to 3.30pm in
the Winter). Trains on Thursdays are diesel-hauled.
Prices: Adult £8.00
　　　　Child £4.00 (Under 5's travel free)
　　　　Senior Citizen £5.00
　　　　Family £20.00 (2 adults + 2 children)

Detailed Directions by Car:
Sunniside Station is off the A6076 Sunniside to Stanley road in Co. Durham. To reach the Railway, leave A1(M),
follow signs for Beamish museum at Chester-le-Street then continue to Stanley and follow Tanfield Railway signs.

TELFORD STEAM RAILWAY

Address: The Old Loco Shed, Bridge Road, Horsehay, Telford, Shropshire
Telephone Enquiries: 07876 762790
Year Formed: 1976
Location: Horsehay & Dawley Station
Length of Line: ½ mile standard gauge, an eighth of a mile 2 foot narrow gauge

N° of Steam Locos: 5
N° of Other Locos: 12
N° of Members: Approximately 220
Annual Membership Fee: £12.00
Approx N° of Visitors P.A.: 10,000
Web site: www.telfordsteamrailway.co.uk

GENERAL INFORMATION

Nearest Mainline Station: Wellington or Telford Central
Nearest Bus Station: Dawley (1 mile)
Car Parking: Free parking at the site
Coach Parking: Free parking at the site
Souvenir Shop(s): 'Freight Stop Gift Shop'
Food & Drinks: 'The Furnaces' Tea Room

SPECIAL INFORMATION

Telford Steam Railway has both a Standard Gauge and Narrow Gauge line as well as Miniature and Model Railways. Major line extension works are currently underway.

OPERATING INFORMATION

Opening Times: Every Sunday and Bank Holiday between Easter and the end of September. Santa Specials run in December. Open 11.00am to 4.30pm.
Steam Working: 2 foot gauge on all operating days. Standard gauge on the last Sunday of the month, every Sunday in August and also on Bank Holidays.
Prices: Adult all day tickets £3.00
Child all day tickets £3.00
Family all day tickets £12.00

Detailed Directions by Car:
From All Parts: Exit the M54 at Junction 6, travel south along the A5223 then follow the brown tourist signs for the railway.

Tyseley Locomotive Works Visitor Centre

Address: 670 Warwick Road, Tyseley, Birmingham B11 2HL
Telephone Nº: (0121) 708-4960
Year Formed: 1969
Location of Museum: Tyseley
Length of Line: One third of a mile

Nº of Steam Locos: Varies with visiting Locos and restoration contracts
Nº of Members: Approximately 600
Approx Nº of Visitors P.A.: 10,000
Gauge: Standard
Web site: www.vintagetrains.co.uk

GENERAL INFORMATION

Nearest Mainline Station: Tyseley (5 mins. walk)
Nearest Bus Station: Birmingham. Bus Stop at Reddings Lane – 2 minutes walk (Bus route 37 passes the entrance)
Car Parking: 200 spaces at Railway site
Coach Parking: Space at Railway site
Souvenir Shop(s): Yes
Food & Drinks: None

SPECIAL INFORMATION

The Museum runs a large workshop which produces refurbished locomotives, many for operation on Network Rail Lines.

OPERATING INFORMATION

Opening Times: 2010 dates: The Museum open days will be held on 26th and 27th June between the hours of 10.00am and 4.00pm. Further events are planned later in the year. Please contact the museum for further information.
Steam Working: On all open days. The Loco Works also operates mainline excursions from the Museum Station and runs the Shakespeare Express from Birmingham to Stratford-upon-Avon every Sunday from 4th July to 12th September 2010.
Prices: Vary depending on the open day. Shakespeare Express fares start from around £17.50.

Detailed Directions by Car:
From the North: Exit the M6 at Junction 6 and take A41 ring road towards Solihull; From the South: Exit the M42 at Junction 5 and take the A41 towards Birmingham.

THE WEARDALE RAILWAY

Address: Stanhope Station, Stanhope, Bishop Auckland DL13 2YS	**Nº of Steam Locos**: 2
Telephone Nº: (01388) 526203	**Nº of Other Locos**: 3
Year Formed: 1993	**Nº of Members**: 850
Location: Stanhope to Wolsingham, County Durham	**Approx Nº of Visitors P.A.**: 25,000
	Gauge: Standard
Length of Line: 5½ miles at present	**Web site**: www.weardale-railway.org.uk

GENERAL INFORMATION

Nearest Mainline Station: Bishop Auckland (8½ miles)
Nearest Bus Station: Bishop Auckland (8½ miles)
Car Parking: Available at both Stanhope and Wolsingham Stations
Coach Parking: Available at Wolsingham Station
Souvenir Shop(s): Yes
Food & Drinks: Yes – Signal Box Cafe, Stanhope

SPECIAL INFORMATION

Weardale is in the heart of the North Pennines and the railway provides magnificent unspoilt views. The area is known for its footpaths and bridleways and the railway provides a useful base for walks between stations along banks of the beautiful River Wear.

OPERATING INFORMATION

Opening Times: 2010 dates: Daily from 16th July to 5th September. Also open on weekends throughout the year and a number of other midweek dates. Trains run from 10.30am to 4.30pm in the Summer and from 10.30am to 3.30pm in the Winter. Please contact the railway for further information.
Steam Working: No specific dates – trains may be Steam or diesel-hauled.
Prices: Adult Return £8.00 (Day Rover £10.00)
  Child Return £4.00 (Day Rover £6.00)
  Senior Citizen Return £6.00 (Rover £8.00)

Detailed Directions by Car:
From All Parts: Stanhope Station is located in Stanhope, just off the A689; Wolsingham Station is located in Wolsingham, also just off the A689.

WENSLEYDALE RAILWAY

Address: Leeming Bar Station, Leases Road, Leeming Bar, Northallerton DL7 9AR	**Nº of Steam Locos**: Visiting locos only
Telephone Nº: 08454 50 54 74	**Nº of Other Locos**: Various Diesel locos
Year Formed: The railway association was formed in 1990, the Railway PLC in 2000.	**Nº of Members**: 3,500
	Annual Membership Fee: £15.00
	Approx Nº of Visitors P.A.: –
Location of Line: Leeming Bar to Redmire	**Gauge**: Standard
Length of Line: Approximately 16 miles	**Web site**: www.wensleydalerailway.com

GENERAL INFORMATION

Nearest Mainline Station: Northallerton (7 miles)
Nearest Bus Station: Northallerton (7 miles)
Car & Coach Parking: Available at Leeming Bar, Leyburn and Redmire Stations
Souvenir Shop(s): Yes
Food & Drinks: At Leeming Bar & Leyburn stations.

SPECIAL INFORMATION

Most services are operated via DMU and travel to Leyburn & Redmire tourist destinations in the Wensleydale Valley. Other heritage diesel groups also use the line.

OPERATING INFORMATION

Opening Times: Weekends only during off-peak time plus other days over Christmas and New Year. Open daily during the summer. Please contact the railway for further information.
Steam Working: A visiting steam locomotive will operate between 17th July and 30th August 2010.
Prices: Adult Day Rover £12.50
        Child Day Rover £6.50
        Senior Citizen Day Rover £11.50
        Family Day Rover £22.00 – £32.00
Note: Single and return tickets cost less than Day Rovers. Prices may differ during steam working.

Detailed Directions by Car:
From All Parts: Exit the A1 at the Leeming Bar exit and take the A684 towards Northallerton. The station is on the left after about ¼ mile close to the road junction and after the traffic lights.   By Bus: The Dales & District 73 bus route travels between Northallerton and Leeming Bar.

West Somerset Railway

Address: The Railway Station, Minehead, Somerset   TA24 5BG
Telephone Nº: (01643) 704996 (enquiries)
Year Formed: 1976
Location of Line: Bishops Lydeard (near Taunton) to Minehead
Length of Line: 19¾ miles

Nº of Steam Locos: 7
Nº of Other Locos: 12
Nº of Members: 5,000
Annual Membership Fee: £17.00
Approx Nº of Visitors P.A.: 220,000
Gauge: Standard
Web site: www.west-somerset-railway.co.uk

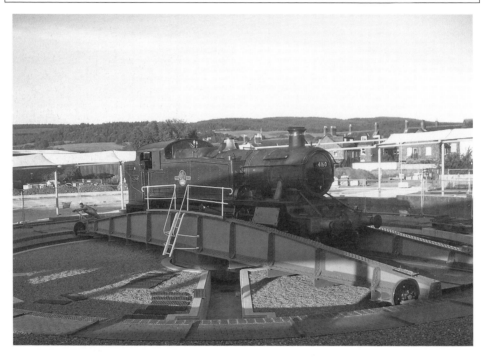

GENERAL INFORMATION

Nearest Mainline Station: Taunton (4 miles)
Nearest Bus Station: Taunton (4½ miles) – Services 18 & 28 run to Bishops Lydeard.
Car Parking: Free parking at Bishops Lydeard; Council car parking at Minehead and Watchet
Coach Parking: As above
Souvenir Shop(s): Yes – at Minehead, Bishops Lydeard and Washford
Food & Drinks: Yes – At some stations. Buffet and Dining cars on all trains.

SPECIAL INFORMATION

Britain's longest Standard gauge Heritage railway runs through the Quantock Hills and along the Bristol Channel Coast. The line passes through no fewer than ten Stations with museums at Washford and Blue Anchor and a turntable at Minehead.

OPERATING INFORMATION

Opening Times: 2010 dates: Various dates from February to December including daily from 27th April to 3rd October. Open 9.30am to 5.30pm. Please contact the railway for more detailed dates.
Steam Working: All operating days except during Diesel Galas.
Prices: Adult Day Rover £14.80
     Child Day Rover £7.40
     Family Rover £42.00 (2 adult + 4 child)
     Senior Citizen Day Rover £13.40

Detailed Directions by Car:
Exit the M5 at Taunton (Junction 25) and follow signs for A358 to Williton and then the A39 for Minehead. In Minehead, brown tourist signs give directions to the railway.

Whitwell & Reepham Railway

Address: Whitwell Road, Reepham, Norfolk NR10 4GA	**Nº of Steam Locos:** 1
Telephone Nº: (01603) 871694	**Nº of Other Locos:** 1
Year Formed: 2009	**Nº of Members:** Approximately 400
Location of Line: Norfolk	**Annual Membership Fee:** £15.00
Length of Line: Almost ½ mile	**Approx Nº of Visitors P.A.:** 6,000
	Gauge: Standard
	Web site: www.whitwellstation.com

GENERAL INFORMATION

Nearest Mainline Station: Norwich (15 miles)
Nearest Bus Station: Norwich (15 miles)
Car Parking: Available on site
Coach Parking: Available
Souvenir Shop(s): Yes
Food & Drinks: Available

SPECIAL INFORMATION

Whitwell & Reepham Station re-opened on the 28th February 2009 nearly 50 years after it was closed to passengers on 2nd March 1959. The intention is to restore the Station to its former glory, re-laying of track and sidings, acquiring rolling stock and setting up a museum relating to the Station and The Midland & Great Northern Railway.

OPERATING INFORMATION

Opening Times: Weekends throughout the year from 10.00am until dusk.
Steam Working: Usually the first Sunday each month and also on Bank Holidays. Please contact the Museum for further details.
Prices: Adults £2.00
  Children £1.00
  Family £5.00
Note: Prices shown above are for train rides – admission to the museum is free of charge.

Detailed Directions by Car:
From All Parts: Take the A1067 Norwich to Fakenham Road to Bawdeswell then follow the B1145 to Reepham. The railway is located about 1 mile to the South-west of Reepham and is well-signposted.

YEOVIL RAILWAY CENTRE

Address: Yeovil Junction Station, Stoford, Yeovil   BA22 9UU
Telephone Nº: (01935) 410420
Year Formed: 1993
Location of Line: Yeovil Junction
Length of Line: ¼ mile
Gauge: Standard

Nº of Steam Locos: 1
Nº of Other Locos: 3
Nº of Members: 300
Annual Membership Fee: £12.50
Approx Nº of Visitors P.A.: 5,000
Web site:
www.yeovilrailway.freeservers.com

GENERAL INFORMATION

Nearest Mainline Station: Yeovil Junction (adjacent)
Nearest Bus Station: A regular bus service runs from Yeovil Bus Station (2 miles)
Car Parking: Available on site
Coach Parking: Available nearby
Souvenir Shop(s): Yes
Food & Drinks: Available

SPECIAL INFORMATION

The Visitor Centre is located in a GWR Transfer Shed which was built in 1864.
The centre also runs Driver Experience days.

OPERATING INFORMATION

Opening Times: Open regularly for Steam Train days, Mainline steam visits and other special events from March to October. Also open for Santa Specials in December and for static viewing every Sunday morning from 10.00am until noon. Please contact the Centre for further details of event days.
Steam Working: The Yeovil 150 Celebration is on the 17th & 18th July 2010. Please contact the Centre for further details.
Prices: Adult £5.00
          Child £2.50 (Ages 5 to 15)
Note: Prices shown above are for Steam Working days.

Detailed Directions by Car:
The Centre is part of Yeovil Junction Station which is served by South West Trains. By road simply follow the signs to Yeovil Junction Station from Yeovil town centre or from the A37 Dorchester to Yeovil road. The entrance to Yeovil Railway Centre is through the low bridge, half way up the Yeovil Junction Station approach road.